BY THE EDITORS OF CONSUMER GUIDE®

CARS
That Never Were

Beekman House
New York

Contents

Library of Congress Catalog Card Number: 80-84038
ISBN: 0-517-309939

Published by:
Beekman House
A Division of Crown Publishers, Inc.
One Park Avenue
New York, N.Y. 10016

Chief Contributing Author: Richard M. Langworth
Contributing Authors: Jeff Godshall, Jan Norbye,
Graham Robson
Photo Credits: Richard M. Langworth, William L. Bailey,
Jeff Godshall, Neil Perry, Don Butler, *Special Interest Autos*
magazine, Brooks Stevens Design Associates, Taylor-
Constantine
Jacket Illustration: Timothy Burkhardt
Book Designer: Frank E. Peiler

Introduction

Who says cars *have* to run on four wheels: what's the matter with, say, three? Did you ever hear of a 1948 four-door sedan—with a 166-bhp, rear-mounted, air-cooled engine—that would do 135 mph and 0-60 in 10 seconds? If Packard hadn't run out of money, what would its 1957-58-59 models have looked like? If Brooks Stevens had convinced Studebaker to build what he called the "Familia," could we have had an economy compact priced at $1085? And whatever happened to the *1958* Continental Mark II?

These are some of the questions answered in this book, the story of some 26 prototypes and also-rans—the intriguing cars that never were. They span a period of about 40 years, from Ford's and Chrysler's would-be 1943-44-45 models, to the dream car that was once scheduled to become the 1980 Corvette.

Enthusiasts have always been fascinated by cars that almost made it. They tend to evoke visions of unfettered engineers and imaginative stylists conjuring up earth-shaking ideas, only to be frustrated at the last minute by the Dark Forces of corporate politics and economics. Too often, though, such stillborn projects are made to seem more important historically than they really were. Some of the cars profiled in these pages have been hailed as designs that could have "saved" Studebaker—or Kaiser, Packard, Hudson, or any number of others. In fact, they were merely plans for the next generation of those makes. By themselves, they probably could not have helped those companies survive. The automakers that have disappeared since World War II did so for complex, long-standing

reasons. Their ultimate destiny would not have been changed by the appearance of a single design.

Nevertheless, it's interesting to look at some of these proposals on their own merit (or lack thereof) as cars. Some would have signaled dramatic shifts in their makers' design or marketing philosophy. The 1962 DeSoto, for example, would have been "downsized" (to use a latter-day term) like the 1962 Dodge and Plymouth actually were. The odds are that this wouldn't have helped DeSoto any more than it did Dodge and Plymouth. Even more interesting are the plans for scaled-down Chryslers and Imperials that year, despite the company's then-current claim that it would "never produce a small Chrysler."

The Henry Js intended for 1955 and later would have been a considerable improvement on the 1951-54 production models, and probably would have scored higher sales. The 1955 Willys might have brought the first hardtop-station wagon. The 1955 Hudson (the one planned before the hardy independent company merged with Nash) would have been a lot different from most other cars on the road—lower, lighter, and with many unique touches. But if it had been sold with a six-cylinder engine like the Hudsons before it, it probably would have flopped just like they did. The 1952 Frazer, had it seen production, would have been a nice luxury version of the lovely '51 Kaiser, but some of the ideas for the '56 Kaiser were better forgotten, as you'll see. The proposed 1958 Continental Mark II *was* forgotten—unfortunately.

Sprinkled in with these non-starters are several

proposed revivals—the postwar LaSalles, the Cadillac V-12/V-16 studies of the '60s, the Continental Mark II berline and retractable slated for 1958, and the '56 Packard Request. The last answered customer requests for a return of the classic Packard grille.

Particularly interesting is the wartime styling work done by Ford and Chrysler. (We weren't able to include mid-'40s GM studies, because most of that firm's new designs, introduced in 1942, would have lasted through 1945 if it hadn't been for the war. As it turned out, all-new GM cars didn't appear until 1948, and those resulted from work done after the war years.) It's fascinating to see how both Ford and Chrysler were working along the same lines—curved, streamlined shapes, with skirted wheels and covered or frenched headlights. Virtually all these proposals were passed over after the war as both automakers jumped ahead with brand-new styles for 1949.

Also included here are several projects that didn't get off the ground for a long time—or never did. During and after World War II, Ford and Chevy both started planning low-price compact models. Although roundly criticized over the years for failing to build such cars, Chevy and Ford, according to our research, actually spent vast resources on several occasions getting ready to do just that. What stopped them was the perception that Americans didn't want economy cars—certainly not before 1960, and maybe not really until 1970. Chrysler's turbine cars are another example of an expensive developmental project out of step with buyer tastes, though Chrysler still believes the turbine

has a future. As always, the industry produced the kinds of cars customers were buying or said they wanted. In the '60s, Ford again dabbled with a compact—the Cardinal—but it ended up overseas as the German Ford Taunus 12-M. And that car fell far short of what the company had intended.

You'll also find here some of the wildest "also-rans" in postwar automotive history—the exotic Corvair show cars; the radical, $17,000 Gaylord; the custom-built Jaguar Pirana; and Bill Mitchell's dramatic Aerovette. Because of the sentimental interest in MG and its current woes, we thought it appropriate to include a chapter on two replacements for the MGB. These would have been built were it not for the stonewall opposition from MG's corporate master, British Leyland.

Finally, there's the Tucker, the best-known never-was in history—a car many say was a victim of the big Detroit manufacturers, which is an erroneous idea, in our judgment. The Tucker was revolutionary in many ways, and deserved a better fate than it got. But it was doomed by the actions of the man who built it.

Of course, there will be other cars-that-never-were in the future—some of them are in the making as you read this. Space limitations prevent the inclusion of more recent no-shows like Ford's two-seat *1980 Thunderbird*, for example. At this writing, the industry rumor mill says there may yet be a LaSalle in our future, and perhaps even a DeLorean. Time will tell. One thing's for sure: there's bound to be plenty of material for a sequel to this volume.

Great Expectations:

Cadillac's Postwar V-12 and V-16

The greatest Cadillacs of the Classic era—perhaps the greatest of all time—were the fabled V-16s of the 1930s. Their engine was perhaps the most significant powerplant to emerge during the decade. Introduced in 1930, it preceded every other domestic multi-cylinder engine by at least a year—and it was a *sixteen,* not a twelve or a mere glorified eight. With the V-16, Cadillac capitalized on tremendous international interest in multi-cylinder supercars. In fact, it was the only company that really profited with such a model. Before buyer demand tailed off in mid-1930, the division had shipped over 2000 V-16 models—more than the entire three-year production run of the 16-cylinder Marmon. Cadillac's arch-rival

Packard didn't produce an engine with more than eight cylinders until 1932, and that was "only" a V-12. By then, Cadillac had a V-12 as well, and its multi-cylinder models handily outsold Packard's.

After World War II, twelve- and sixteen-cylinder engines were temporarily forgotten. The development of high-octane gasoline made more powerful high-compression engines possible, and hastened the emergence of efficient overhead-valve V-8s like Cadillac's outstanding "331" of 1949. Literally all the engine technology of the late '30s and the '40s went into developing this type of powerplant. After the war, there was no longer any need for more than eight cylinders.

By the middle '50s, the ohv V-8 had become the favorite engine in American cars. In the luxury field, Chrysler had it in its 1951 Imperial; Lincoln adopted it in 1952. Even Packard, long the most conservative of luxury-car manufacturers, discarded its L-head straight eight for an ohv V-8 in 1955. Once the V-8 was

Early proposals for the V-16 were based on 1963 production styling. Fastback roof taper was dramatic.

Photographed in September 1963 at the GM Tech Center, this scale model had outlandish proportions.

established, however, engineers were free to engage in a little conjecture. Again, thoughts turned to an engine of 12 or 16 cylinders, but designed with modern, high-compression, overhead-valve heads.

Packard had actually installed at least one prewar V-12 in a postwar car, a 1951 Patrician, at the request of one wealthy customer. During 1955, Packard began considering a production V-12 as an offshoot of its new ohv V-8. According to former product planner Richard Stout, the plan was to use the basic V-8 tooling with a 50-percent longer block to contain the four extra cylinder bores. Since the V-8 block was a 90-degree "Y," 30-degrees out of phase for the in-step firing needed for a V-12, each rod thrown would be split and staggered 30 degrees to compensate. The same "split-throw" principle was later used by Buick to create its 90-degree V-6 of the early '60s.

Packard's overhead-valve V-12 would have had a displacement of 480 cubic inches, impressive indeed. But as Dick Stout remembered, "It was strictly grandstand stuff . . . Tooling was guesstimated in the $750,000 area—modest for such a spectacular result . . . But in the end the money just wasn't there." Studebaker-Packard, facing imminent bankruptcy, wrapped up the luxury Packards after 1956, and built low- to medium-priced Studebaker-based cars through the marque's end in 1958.

About six years after Packard's try at a multi-cylinder engine, Cadillac Division got the same idea. Here, research took two different paths: a fairly crude, "bolted together" V-16 composed of two small-displacement V-8s; and an exotic, all-new V-12 with overhead camshafts.

The V-16 was probably not designed around Cadillac's own V-8. By 1960, its displacement was close to 400 cid, which would have made a two-block engine

simply enormous. A more likely choice was Chevrolet's 283, which in V-16 form would have displaced 566 cubic inches. According to Chuck Jordan, who worked on the styling side of the V-16 revival, this engine was more a flight of fancy than a formal engineering project. "We were working with Engineering Staff to put two V-8s together," Jordan related. "It was kind of a home-made way to do it, but it was just to project an image we wanted to get across to Cadillac at the time. Nothing serious was ever developed engineering-wise."

More interesting was the clean-slate V-12 being planned at the same time by Cadillac engineers. According to Jordan, "this was a very sophisticated powerplant, and quite beautiful. I'm sure it was designed from scratch as an overhead-cam engine—a very exciting piece of machinery to see." It was a 90-degree unit, constructed on the Buick V-6 principle for in-step firing.

Whether the ohc V-12 or the less-likely, two-block V-16 ever had a chance of production remains unclear. What is clear is that engineering for both never progressed beyond the prototype stage. But Jordan and his fellow stylists did come up with a remarkable series of design proposals for a multi-cylinder Cadillac. The first scale models were based on 1963 production styling. Gradually, work proceeded through scale and full-size fiberglass models designed from the ground up.

The late '50s had seen two ultra-posh supercars with price tags to match—the perennial Ford-GM struggle carried to the upper reaches of the luxury market. The first was a latter-day Continental, the Mark II of 1956. Ford Motor Company had toyed with reviving the Continental since the last 1948 model left the production line. But the idea was left on the back burner while

Great Expectations

the company reorganized along more profitable lines in the early '50s. Because that had taken a lot of effort and money, it wasn't until 1952 that Ford set up its Special Products Division, and the updated Continental finally got off the ground.

The Mark II was a beautiful design, the work of Ford's own Special Products stylists headed by John Rinehart and directed by William Clay Ford. Priced at $10,000, the Mark II captured most of the automotive headlines at the time—which was precisely Ford's intent. The car was not supposed to make a profit: its main purpose was to wrest away Cadillac's title as the country's most prestigious luxury make. In those hotly competitive years, GM was naturally not about to take Ford's new challenger lying down. Within weeks of learning about the forthcoming Mark II, Cadillac began development of what became the 1957 Eldorado Brougham.

Priced at $13,074, the Brougham was very different in character than the Continental. While the Mark II was conservative in appearance, the Brougham was brash, sporting fashionable tailfins, sparkling "sabre spoke" wheels, and a brushed aluminum roof. Because the Continental was a close-coupled two-door hardtop, the Brougham had to be a close-coupled *four*-door hardtop. It featured rear doors hinged at the rear, as on a Lancia that GM's Harley Earl had seen and admired in Italy. While the Mark II used a conventional suspension, the Brougham rode on air bags.

Neither the Mark II nor the Eldorado Brougham sold in anything like profitable volume. For this reason, both were quickly revised to be more practical, or at least salable, products. For 1958, Lincoln fielded the Mark III, much lower in price and with a variety of body styles including a four-door. For 1959-60, Cadillac farmed out Brougham body manufacture to Pininfarina in Italy, and dropped the model entirely for '61 as unprofitable and unnecessary.

Another 1963 idea shows beginnings of 1966 Toronado/Riviera themes.

Overhead view shows cantilevered roof with radically wrapped windshield.

However, that didn't prevent the designers from dreaming up new and intriguing "ultimate" Cadillacs. In fact, the temper of the times encouraged it. There were no government standards yet for fuel economy, crash protection, or exhaust emissions. Gasoline, if it cost 25¢ a gallon, cost a lot. A new, long-hooded, ultra-exotic Cadillac, even if it was nothing more than a show car, could be something of wonder.

Chuck Jordan, who supplied the photographs shown here, emphasizes that there was no thought of actual production: "It was a two-passenger Cad with 16 cylinders, alright—but it was done just to make a

The August 1963 scale model was a ground-up design and obviously owed little to contemporary Cadillacs.

By December 1965, the V-16 had an official project code: XP-840. This was as far as it went.

Full-size mockup with complete interior shows how far the V-16 idea was taken. Front fenders stand away from the body at their rear edges.

statement about the heritage of Cadillac and where we were going with the image—the return to the long hood.

"We built several scale models and one full-size clay. The concept of all was invariably the same—a long-hooded car to contain the long engine. These designs were exaggerated—almost cartoon-like—but exciting to work on. This was one of our pet advanced projects at the time.

"Some of the [customized] cars being done now, chopped and extended, actually have some of that quality, but they all look homemade. I think these models, in contrast, were very well executed.

"We finally dropped the project after the full-size 1965 model was completed. We had a lot of other things to do, and here we were playing with a full-size clay we never intended to expose. It was strictly a styling exercise."

Of course, it is just such styling exercises like these that fire the dreams of car enthusiasts. Imagine a production Cadillac that looked like one of these models. Even if it had a conventional V-8 lost under that long hood, it would have been a very impressive piece, indeed.

Dated March 1965, this rendering by stylist Wayne Cady shows another approach to the V-12/V-16. Note "sedanca" roof.

9

Even in the late '40s, small-car projects were nothing new for Chevrolet. Since the early '30s, the division had, from time to time, designed and tested small models of its own or for GM's European divisions, Opel in Germany and Vauxhall in England. The Cadet was different. Seriously intended as a new domestic model, it was quite advanced for its day. But it never had a chance. By GM tradition and logic, the Cadet was *too* different. This not only led to embarrassing comparisons with then-current Chevys, but also posed difficulties on the production side. Anything that called for new manufacturing methods or production line changes was generally doomed.

During World War II, all the Big Three automakers instituted small-car studies. In 1943, General Motors executives were fairly certain of an Allied victory, but were unsure of what the postwar economy would be like. All remembered the depression following World War I. They also knew the nation's commitment to this war effort was far greater, industry's swing to war production was total, and a staggering number of military personnel would be returning. In short, there were sound reasons to fear an economic downturn when defense orders dried up and veterans glutted the civilian job market.

If purchasing power was going to be a problem, price would be the main factor in postwar car sales. Therefore, Chevrolet decided it had to have a smaller, cheaper model priced competitively, if not lower than, expected smaller cars from Ford and Plymouth.

Before the war, cars had been priced at about 50 cents per pound. Measuring "value" in this way had led to the industry's idea that to make a car more cheaply you had to make it lighter. Chevrolet had already attempted to cut production costs by combining several parts into one, simplifying assembly methods, and using other tricks that worked on cars of all sizes. There seemed little else it could do to keep the same profit margin on a smaller model.

All these considerations played a part in GM's

Chevrolet Cadet:

It Never Had a Chance

decision to pursue the small-car project later code-named Cadet. To be built and sold by Chevrolet, the Cadet would offer practical all-around transportation in a smaller-size package for a one-car family on a budget. It wasn't meant to be as tiny as, say, a Crosley or a Bantam, but closer in size to the Willys American of 1941, and two of GM's own European models—the Vauxhall Fourteen and the Opel Kapitän—both powered by small six-cylinder engines.

The Opel and Vauxhall were considered quite up-to-date when they appeared in 1939. Even though the war had made time stand still for automotive designers, they all knew that their prewar models would soon seem old-hat in the postwar market. Any car company has to think ahead when planning a totally new model. The design must be flexible enough so it can be facelifted and reskinned several times without basic, expensive changes. The small Chevy was slated to run for up to 20 years without fundamental change. But, GM had nothing to use as a starting point for its postwar small car—or even a clear idea of what it should be like.

The GM Engineering Staff, responsible for developing advanced concepts for the various divisions, had

no small car in the works while Charles L. McCuen was in charge from 1940 to 1947. McCuen, a former Oldsmobile engineer and general manager, was well aware of GM chairman Alfred P. Sloan's dislike of small cars, and carefully steered clear of them. Fortunately, Chevrolet had an Englishman named Alex Taub. Taub had arrived in the mid-'20s after holding important engineering posts with several British companies. He helped design and develop the 1929 Chevy Six, and spent the next four or five years arguing the merits of smaller, lighter, less conventionally engineered cars. He got some projects started, but was then transferred to Vauxhall to oversee a total rejuvenation of that firm's model line. When he returned to the U.S., he became involved in war-production programs and never returned to Chevrolet. But he had left his mark.

Carrying on where Taub left off was Earle S. MacPherson, an idealistic engineer full of radical ideas. MacPherson was always looking for ways to improve a car's general layout and makeup, as well as its individual parts. His approach was intellectual, methodical, and practical. MacPherson had left Hupmobile in 1934 after 12 years to join the GM Engineering Staff. Previously, he had worked for Chalmers, Liberty, Harley-Davidson, Pierce-Arrow, and Studebaker. He joined Chevrolet in 1935. His first assignment was to design a light car, but it never got to the production stage. Not much is known about it, though it was probably unrelated to what became the Cadet.

MacPherson soon formed his own experimental group at Chevrolet, working independently of current programs. That was fine with chief engineer James M. Crawford, who was scared of innovation, and seemed

Chevrolet Cadet

to harbor a strange insecurity about his own ideas. These two men would tangle when the Cadet program was nearing completion and production was drawing near.

The Cadet was born because Marvin E. Coyle, then Chevrolet general manager, was worried about the postwar market. It's not clear how much he knew about Ford's and Chrysler's small-car plans. Coyle hardly bothered with market research, and seemed disinterested in finding out what the competition was up to. His background was mainly financial, and he turned out to be a very competent administrator. So, it was not his enthusiasm for small cars that led him to support the Cadet. But after listening long and carefully to MacPherson, Coyle thought such a car could be a necessity in the postwar market should his pessimistic visions of an economic downturn come true. Naturally, MacPherson stressed the potential to cut costs in a small car when he talked to Coyle.

Junior engineers, such as Donald McPherson (no relation), were dazzled by MacPherson's imagination and near-obsession with lightness and simplicity. (Donald McPherson, now general manager of Buick, admits he never forgot the lessons learned from his illustrious mentor.) MacPherson's group was a stimulating environment for engineering thought and reflection. It was disbanded during the war while he worked on military equipment assignments, but was reactivated in the spring of 1945, before VE-day.

Without having a specific design in mind, much less on paper, Coyle went to GM president Charles E. ("Engine Charlie") Wilson and sold him on the small-car idea. He secured Wilson's backing, against expected opposition from Sloan and Crawford, by asking

Wilson to announce (on May 15, 1945) that Chevrolet was planning to offer a new economy car. Coyle then called in Crawford, who reluctantly appointed MacPherson as chief of the Light Car Project. Now, things began to hum. With his newfound authority, MacPherson put together a team of the ablest engineers he could find. Bored with their old routine, Chevrolet engineers from other departments were soon knocking on his door to get in on the Light Car Project. But MacPherson kept the group small and manageable. He also thought through every detail of the evolving design.

The Cadet was not a warmed-over prewar car, nor a collection of random improvements. Its design was dictated by pure logic. What was so extraordinary about it? Careful attention to weight distribution was one thing. It had a low frame and an even lower driveline for a low center of gravity. The transmission was placed under the front seat, attached via a torque tube to the engine's flywheel housing. The engine was raised at the front, tilting down at the rear, to get the clutch as low as possible. Because of this, the flywheel was split in two, with one half carried on the front end of the crankshaft, and a similar disc providing a face for the clutch at the rear end. All this gave the Cadet a low, flat floor, and an overall height of just 60 inches—quite low for the day.

The design called for 12-inch wheels with fat tires, and a relatively long wheelbase of 108 inches. But the Cadet's most important feature was its all-independent suspension. Chevrolet had had an independent front end since 1934. But because of its greater cost, MacPherson prepared for opposition to an independent *rear* suspension. Its advantages were also not readily apparent on paper, especially to a man like Coyle. So, MacPherson shrewdly prepared two comparison cars: one with torque-tube drive to the rear axle, the other with a conventional Hotchkiss arrange-

Cadet displays the bulbous "bathtub" look typical of the late '40s. The enclosed front wheels would have hampered maneuverability.

ment. A short spin proved the superiority of the independent design for ride comfort, cornering control, and traction.

The Cadet's suspension was a new type, and MacPherson applied for a patent on it (filed March 21, 1947, and granted January 6, 1953). It has since been widely copied on cars of all sizes, and is still known as the MacPherson strut system.

Briefly, the key innovation of this setup was that it eliminated an upper control arm. In its place was a tall spring leg or strut, mounted on a bracket extending from the wheel hub, and attached at its upper end to the bodyshell itself. For the Cadet (and the patent drawings), MacPherson simplified the arrangement even further by making the stabilizer bar do double duty as a structural part of the lower control arms. The same design was used for both the front and rear suspension on the Cadet, except that the rear wheel hubs were locked in place and carried radius arms for transmitting drive thrust. The front wheel hubs used the spring leg as an extended kingpin and steering axis. Narrow-diameter coil springs anchored at the top end were wrapped around the legs, which incorporated hydraulic shock absorbers inside their lower portions.

Elements of MacPherson-type suspensions had been seen before. A French car, the Cottin-Desgouttes of 1926, had spring legs, but used a transverse leaf spring instead of coils. A Fiat engineer named Martinotti took out an Italian patent in 1927 for a design that anticipated MacPherson's use of coil springs and the combined stabilizer bar/lower control arm, but Fiat never used it on a production model.

The engine was probably the Cadet's least interesting feature. It was an overhead-valve six, smaller than Chevy's beloved "stovebolt," but outwardly a lot like it. Unlike the old-fashioned "stovebolt," the Cadet unit was a modern short-stroke design, with a high-compression cylinder head—just like the Oldsmobile and Cadillac V-8s of 1948-49. (The Cadet would have had these features in 1947, if all had gone according to plan.) With a 7.25:1 compression ratio, the little six put out 64.5 bhp at 4000 rpm from its 132.6 cubic inches. The valve gear was fairly standard, with a side camshaft, pushrods, and rockers. Different types of pistons were tried, from domed to flat-topped. A wedge-type was finally selected as providing the best combustion characteristics under varying operating conditions. The engine weighed only two-thirds as much as the "stovebolt" six in the Master 85.

The Cadet's dry weight had been pegged at around 2200 pounds. MacPherson miscalculated on brake drum dimensions, however, and prototype test models proved quite deficient in stopping power. That would have been an easy matter to fix if the project had been given the go-ahead. But the Cadet was running into snags, and the most troublesome one was cost.

Coyle's idea had been to market the Cadet with a retail price under $1000. But it was soon obvious it would cost that much—and perhaps more—just to build. Coyle's pessimistic prognostications for the national economy proved unfounded when the Truman administration pursued an expansionist policy. Up to 1950, the auto industry had to go all out just to catch up with pent-up buyer demand for new cars. It was the era of the seller's market. But estimates on the Cadet's production costs were disturbing. After the war, raw material prices had increased greatly, doubling in some cases. Wages were up, too, knocking a hole in the earlier cost/profit calculations. All this was quite a blow to the Cadet.

A further blow came when Coyle was promoted to vice-president in charge of the car and truck group, and Nicholas E. Dreystadt was transferred from Cadillac to take over at Chevrolet. Dreystadt had no ties to the small-car project, and got only unfavorable comment on it from Crawford, who was now corporate engineering vice-president. The division's new chief engineer, John G. Wood, didn't support it either.

But, MacPherson didn't give up. Heading back to the drawing board, he tried to reduce the Cadet's production costs by redesigning details. For example, he suspended the foot pedals from pivot points up in the cowl area instead of using stems anchored to a pivot shaft under the floor. Instead of mechanical linkages, the clutch and brake systems were operated by hydraulic cylinders mounted next to the pivot arms—another of MacPherson's ideas that has since become commonplace. He was even prepared to sacrifice the independent rear suspension. But no ordinary replacement would do. If there had to be a live axle layout, it would have to be as simple as possible. His answer was single-leaf springs, tapered to vary in both thickness and width.

After new cost studies were made, the corporation's financial experts began looking at the car's sales and profit potential. With a higher price, but still significantly under that of the standard Chevrolet, it was estimated the Cadet could not make a profit for GM with annual sales of less than 300,000 units. Chevrolet's sales volume had reached 880,000 cars in 1941, but fell to only 330,000 in 1946, recovering to 640,000 in 1947. Understandably, the sales organization wasn't eager to have an extra 300,000 Cadets on its hands, and said so.

That sounded the death knell for the Cadet. The GM Engineering Policy Committee sealed its fate in May 1947 by taking it off Chevrolet's hands. The project was transferred to a study group within the corporate engineering staff, where Crawford quietly killed it.

After that, MacPherson saw no future for his ideas at Chevrolet—or anywhere else at General Motors. In September 1947, he joined Ford at the invitation of his friend Harold T. Youngren, the former chief engineer at Oldsmobile who had recently taken over as Dearborn's engineering vice-president. MacPherson then went to England, where he designed the new Consul and Zephyr models that came out in 1950. The Ford Zephyr had a short-stroke high-compression six, MacPherson-strut front suspension, suspended pedals with hydraulic actuation, and 13-inch wheels with fat tires. In other words, it was an updated version of the Cadet that might have been.

Sweet Dreams:
Those Memorable Corvair Specials

The decline and death of the Chevrolet Corvair is one of those sad and intriguing ironies in the history of the American automobile. Here was an efficiently sized, economical, lively car, ideal for today's world and our diminished natural resources. Yet consumer advocates, who might have been expected to welcome such a car, disparaged it.

Ralph Nader cannot be blamed for singlehandedly killing the Corvair. The ax had actually fallen some six months before his book, *Unsafe at Any Speed,* appeared. GM's decision to continue the car after 1965 only until development costs and tooling investment were amortized was based on the success of Ford's Mustang, which overwhelmed Corvair in the market-

place. It was the Mustang and not Nader that forced Chevrolet to rethink its ideas about sporty compacts. That led eventually to the Camaro as its designated Mustang-beater. Of course, the Corvair was technically more advanced than either the Mustang or the Camaro, which partly explains why it continues to inspire car enthusiasts. Today, upwards of 7500 of these air-cooled compacts are on the roster of the Corvair Society of America (CORSA).

Technically interesting cars also tend to excite designers and engineers. During the Corvair's lifetime, many fascinating prototypes, experimentals, and show cars were built using its components. Some of these came surprisingly close to production.

Original Sebring Spyder carried twin racing windscreens and "backbone" divider bar.

A second Sebring Spyder used the stock Corvair windshield, but kept the same racy image.

14

Sebring Spyder, 1961

The first of these Corvairs-that-never-were was the Sebring Spyder, a creation of William L. (Bill) Mitchell and his staff of GM designers. Though the SS at a glance looked merely like a standard Corvair without a top, only its doors were shared with production models. Its wheelbase was just 93 inches, 15 less than stock, so its fenders and hood were somewhat shorter. All body panels were steel, except for a one-piece lift-off fiberglass deck that covered both the engine compartment and an upholstered luggage space behind the twin bucket seats. A center divider strip extended

forward from the leading edge of this tonneau cover to the dash, helping to "compartmentalize" the interior.

The Sebring Spyder had a heavy-duty factory suspension kit, a special front anti-sway bar, and extra-heavy spring/shock settings. The rear wheels had two degrees of negative camber (versus zero camber on stock models). The engine, tweaked by Corvette engineer Zora Arkus-Duntov, would rev freely to its 5800-rpm redline. GM never released horsepower ratings, but the SS powerplant would certainly have been well ahead of the regular Corvair's optional 98-bhp high-performance engine. In other words, the Spyder would have been a rocket.

Like many experimentals before it, the Sebring Spyder was, in fact, a preview of a forthcoming production model, the turbocharged Monza Spyder of 1962-64. The Monza Spyder used stock body panels, of course, and shared the regular 108-inch wheelbase with the rest of the line. But its multi-gauge dashboard was right out of the SS, and much was learned about the tuning potential of the Corvair engine with this famous prototype.

Super Spyder, 1962

Less than a year after the Sebring Spyder appeared, GM updated the concept with the Super Spyder. This show machine rode the Sebring Spyder's 93-inch wheelbase, but was vastly different in styling. From the front, it bore a considerable resemblance to the forthcoming 1965 production models, which it obviously influenced. Like its predecessor, the Super Spyder was strictly a two-seater. A padded headrest was built into a tonneau behind the driver's seat, and a pod or bulge tapered out behind it like that of the Jaguar D-type sports/racing car. On each side of the body ahead of the rear wheel openings were three simulated air intakes—a comedown from the Sebring Spyder, which had functional intakes in the same location. Farther to the rear, triple chrome exhaust pipes

The Super Spyder of 1962 was the next Corvair showpiece. Note the racing-type fuel filler on the front fender.

Super Spyder hinted at the '65 Corvair's front-end styling.

Pininfarina's lovely Speciale resides today in Italy.

Sweet Dreams

protruded from behind the rear wheel wells. The Spyder used the 150-bhp turbocharged engine and four-speed transmission from the production Monza Spyder.

In sum, the Super Spyder was a remarkably good-looking car, prettier than the Sebring Spyder, and certainly the most advanced Corvair special produced up to that time. But GM never even hinted it might go into production, and so—unfortunately—it didn't.

Pininfarina Speciale, 1961

A tribute to the broad appeal of the Corvair was the fact that it impressed a lot of Europeans, including those two respected coachmakers, Pininfarina and Bertone. Typically, each bodybuilder moved in different directions with its Corvair-based designs. Pininfarina's Corvair Speciale was more of a "production" exercise than Bertone's wild Testudo, but both whetted the appetites of Corvair fans. Interestingly, too, both cars survive today.

Though the components and basic chassis of the Speciale coupe were entirely Corvair, the body styling was very Italian—and very Pininfarina. The coachbuilder remodeled the interior by eliminating the standard full-size rear seat in favor of a jump seat positioned more closely behind the twin front buckets. The resulting shorter passenger compartment allowed for considerably more hood and deck length outside. The cockpit was also very light and airy-looking thanks to slim roof pillars, a fairly tall greenhouse, and lots of glass, including a large backlight that sloped down sharply to the rear deck. The hood was angled low between the front fenders in a fashion somewhat like that of the later Porsche 911. The fenders were beautifully curved, and the bodysides were decorated only by a modest full-length creaseline.

Pininfarina displayed the Speciale mainly during the 1961-62 European motor show season, wowing crowds at Paris, Frankfurt, London, and Turin. Originally red with a white interior, it was subsequently painted "bottle" green and fitted with tan upholstery. But the car was strictly an exercise; no production plans were ever proposed. That was too bad, because a lot of people thought the Speciale could have been to Corvair what the Karmann-Ghia was to Volkswagen—

The Speciale appeared in 1961—far enough ahead of time to have inspired the lines of the '65 Corvair?

16

Testudo's rounded rear shows why its name was apt.

This 1963 clay model led to the Corvair Monza GT show car.

a luxurious, close-coupled, Italian-styled two-seater built over a standard chassis and drivetrain. As such, the Speciale would have been the gem of the Corvair line. The Speciale is still owned today by Carrozzeria Pininfarina.

Bertone Testudo, 1962

Like Pininfarina's Speciale, Bertone's Testudo (the name roughly means "turtle") was a styling study built around standard Corvair underpinnings. It was the only such study Bertone ever did, and was probably the most radical of all Corvair one-offs.

Though its chassis was strictly stock, the Testudo's bullet-shaped body was hardly ordinary. It was mostly hood and cockpit, with lines that flowed smoothly back from a pointed nose to an enormous wrapped windshield, then tapered quickly rearward to a clean tail. The backlight was wrapped to the sides, and curved to flow into the roofline. A prominent crease punctuated the fuselage midway up the sides. For passenger access, the front glass area and the body portion below it formed a canopy that lifted upward on hinges placed just aft of the hood. There was no exterior decoration, except for tiny Bertone badges. The Testudo was "all

of a piece"—a sensational shape, clean and pure. Even the headlights were pop-up units, invisible from the sides when not in use.

Bertone owned the Testudo until 1972, when the firm began taking bids at $10,000 and up. The car's present whereabouts are unknown, but it seems certain it was sold to a collector.

Monza GT and SS, 1963

Partly as responses to the Testudo, and partly as clean-slate styling concepts, these fiberglass GM show cars were first displayed at the 1963 New York International Auto Show, where they handily stole the limelight. Though both were designed around Corvair components, there were differences between them. The GT coupe carried its engine ahead of the rear axle line, while the SS roadster had it behind the axle, as in production Corvairs. Both were equipped with four-wheel disc brakes, magnesium alloy wheels of the same design, hydraulically operated clutches, and stock Corvair four-speed gearboxes. Both were two-seaters. Because the seats were fixed, the foot pedals were made adjustable for leg-reach. The GT and SS were bumperless at the front, and very cleanly styled.

Testudo was dramatic from any angle. Full-wraparound windshield and "turtle-back" rear are evident in profile.

Sweet Dreams

Large "clamshell" panels opened to reveal oblong Cibié headlights.

The Monza SS convertible had an 88-inch wheelbase, 20 inches shorter than stock. Like production Corvairs, it featured a small front luggage compartment. Its instrument panel was stark but highly functional, with a large tach and speedometer, plus five auxiliary gauges. The low, racing-type windshield and fixed side windows would have been replaced by a conventional windshield and roll-up windows had a production version materialized.

The Monza GT sat on a 92-inch wheelbase, and its smoothly rounded body was quite aerodynamic. One feature obviously inspired by the Testudo was its lift-up cockpit canopy, which eliminated the need for conventional doors. The whole front portion of the greenhouse, from cowl to front side windows and a lot of sheetmetal below, was hinged as a unit. A separate rear-hinged hatch swung up to reveal the engine compartment. The GT engine had a two-carburetor arrangement for quiet, smooth running; the SS used a four-carburetor setup.

These cars—at least the roadster—came as close as any Corvair one-off to actual production. When they first appeared in April 1963, Ford had not yet released the Mustang. GM advance planners still relied on Corvair as their competitor in the sporty-car field. Had the redesigned 1965 Corvair line competed successfully in that market, it is quite likely a street version of the Monza SS or GT would have appeared by 1967 or '68. GM wouldn't have had to come up with the Camaro, with all the expense that project entailed. But the Mustang sold like nickel hamburgers, and all possible spin-offs of the second-generation Corvair were canceled by mid-summer 1965. That was a shame, because the Mustang wasn't half the sports car these Monzas would have been. As *Road & Track* put it back in 1965: "The enthusiast market sorely needs a boost, and these are two cars that could do it." That's still true today.

Astro I, 1967

Although Corvair development was clearly finished by mid-1965, GM showed other design exercises based on Corvair components in 1967—the Piranha coupe and the exciting Astro I. Neither of these were labeled "Corvair," and both were presented strictly as

Mid-engine Monza GT was one of two Corvair specials displayed in 1963.

Stylistically related to the GT, the Monza SS had strong Corvette overtones.

The young lady is demonstrating the Astro I's extreme lowness–just 35.5 inches from road to roof.

idea cars. The Astro I was the more interesting because it incorporated many advanced features.

This car was so low (it stood only 35.5 inches tall) that conventional seats wouldn't fit. So, GM created "pushbutton positioning": the driver simply stepped inside and touched a button on the console to lower the seat into a partial reclining position as the roof/window canopy closed overhead. The rear-mounted Corvair engine blocked vision astern, so a rear-facing periscope device was fitted instead of a rearview mirror. Visibility ahead and directly to the sides was virtually unobstructed. The body itself was fiberglass, and consisted of only two main sections: a front unit, including fenders and windshield; and a rear assembly comprising the canopy, rear fenders, and deck. The rear section pivoted upward for engine compartment as well as interior access.

The Astro I's powerplant showed what Corvair engines might have been had development continued. Displacing 176 cubic inches, it produced no less than 240 bhp at 7200 rpm, aided by a belt-driven overhead camshaft, hemispherical-head combustion chambers, inclined valves, and twin triple-throat carburetors. As evidence of its performance potential, the Astro's

speedometer read to 160 mph and its tachometer to 9000 rpm. There were also oil pressure, alternator, cylinder head temperature, and fuel gauges.

As with most of its show cars, GM did not release performance figures on the Astro I, but the car would probably have been impressive—on curves and straightaways alike. The suspension used double wishbones front and rear; braking was by discs on all four wheels. The wheels themselves were of an unusual two-piece design. The outer half came off for tire changes, and could be replaced with an alternate rim if an increase in tire width was desired.

Astro I capped GM's seven years of involvement with air-cooled, rear-engined automobiles. What a shame all these experimental Corvairs disappeared without ever seeing production. The rear engine itself has since gone out of favor, of course, rendering these cars somewhat obsolete by modern design standards, which strongly favor front-wheel drive and water-cooled, transversely mounted engines. So, even though these Corvairs aren't the sort of cars we should be building today, we probably should have built them in the '60s and early '70s. They would have enriched the automotive landscape.

Aerovette:
For a Moment, It Was the Next Corvette

Aerovette. Many at Chevrolet remember that car. It was to have been the 1980 Corvette, but a few problems—low production versus the expense of compliance with Federal safety regulations and the depressed North American market at the time were the main ones—prevented it from being built. Too bad, because the Aerovette would have started the '80s with a bang.

Of all the fanciful show cars, of all the advanced styling studies, of all the incredible engineering prototypes that have passed through the GM Technical Center in the past quarter century, the Aerovette—had it been produced—would have been the only one to make it to the street virtually intact. The 1963 Corvette had a lot of the feel of the original Sting Ray prototype; the Monza GT gave much to the second-series Corvair and the Opel GT; the Mako Shark show Corvette led directly to the 1968-and-later Stingray model. But in every case, the production car came out taller, narrower, and somehow dumpier than the original. Not so with Aerovette. According to its creator, former GM vice-president for design William L. Mitchell, "The only difference between the Aerovette and its production derivation was an inch more of headroom. Otherwise it was the same." Hard to believe—but true.

The Aerovette began life in 1968 as the XP-882, one of Zora Arkus-Duntov's long string of mid-engine experiments that started in the late '50s with CERV I and went through CERV II of 1963-64. The XP-882

represented a big engineering breakthrough. The earlier cars had the engine mounted in the conventional longitudinal fashion and bolted to an expensive transaxle. But there was no way Chevrolet could justify the production costs of a purpose-built transaxle just so Corvette engineer Duntov could have a new mid-engine model. His patented solution was to turn the V-8 90 degrees in the chassis. The stock GM Turbo Hydra-matic was nestled on one side of the engine, and was also transversely situated. Driven by a direct chain from the crankshaft, the gearbox was connected to a stock Corvette differential with a short driveshaft that turned a right-angle corner at the front. In this way, it lined up with the "east-west" transmission. To further complicate things, the driveshaft passed through the engine sump encased in a tube. It wasn't an elegant solution, but it worked.

Duntov's high-technology engineering group built two XP-882 coupes in early 1969. Almost on the day they were finished, John Z. DeLorean became Chevrolet general manager and dropped the XP-882 program as being impractical and too expensive. But that decision stood only a year. When Ford announced its intention to import the DeTomaso Pantera from Italy for U.S. sale, DeLorean had one XP-882 cleaned up and exhibited at the New York Auto Show. The car magazines dutifully trumpeted, "the mid-engine Corvette arrives," though nobody at GM had ever said anything about production.

In the early '70s, GM president Ed Cole went crazy over the Wankel rotary engine. Along with the Wankel Vega—which never appeared—Cole had Duntov build an all-new sports car powered by the experimental two-rotor Wankel GM was working on at the time. Styled by Pininfarina, the little mid-engine two-rotor coupe was highly touted as "the next-generation Corvette." In addition, the remaining XP-882 chassis was given a pair of Vega Wankels grafted together to make a four-rotor, 420-bhp supercar. And to visually transform the original XP-882, Duntov persuaded Mitchell to come up with an all-new body for it.

Two-Rotor car (XP-897GT) built by Pininfarina was shown in 1972.

Mid-engine XP-880 prototype was first shown in 1968 as the "Astro II."

Astro II was Chevy's answer to Ford's Mach 2, caused quite a stir among 'Vette fans.

Aerovette

At this point, Mitchell was engaged in a monumental power struggle (witness GM's use of Pininfarina for the two-rotor car) that ended only with DeLorean's departure from the company. Mitchell seized the four-rotor styling assignment as a heaven-sent opportunity for a brilliant power play. The car would *have* to be nothing less than stunning—better than anything DeLorean could buy on the outside.

"Originally," Mitchell recalled, "they were going to let Georgetto Giugiaro do it. This is my example of the opposite of Giugiaro. His cars are all full of angles. He can't draw perspectives, so he makes a side view and a top view. All his cars look like they've been cut from cardboard. You want to stick Tab A into Slot B . . . But the Aerovette had nice contours, soft curves, and still a certain sharpness. It had really good balance . . . a design you could look at from any angle."

The overriding concept of the four-rotor car was aerodynamic penetration. It stood only 44 inches tall and, according to wind tunnel tests, it had a drag coefficient of .325—substantially better than any other car in production right now. It might well have started a trend away from both the boxy "formal" styling of American cars and the angular idiom of the Giugiaro school. Efficient aerodynamics are going to be necessary with the smaller, more tightly emission-controlled engines of the future. The styling of the four-rotor was clearly a harbinger of the 1980s.

The real triumph of this design was its incorporation of masterful efficiency in a sumptuously sensual package. Unlike most cars, it looked right from any angle—high, low, front, rear, top, bottom. The surface transitions were handled so adroitly, so skillfully, and so naturally, that the car avoided any hint of the artificial histrionics that mark the post-1967 production Corvettes.

The body was a taut skin stretched over the people package. Looked at from the side, the car was most remarkable for its proportions: symmetrical not only from side to side, but also from front to back. Except for a hint of a break where the hood and windshield met, the continuous curve of the top to rear deck was almost exactly matched by the continuous curve of the windshield and hood. It was not a pure teardrop shape, but a symmetrical, streamlined mound very nearly triangular in elevation.

From the front or rear, extreme tumblehome gave the same slope-shouldered appearance. There was no indication of whether the car was front- or mid-engine—indeed, the body would suit a chassis of either type. In a sense, the design borrowed something from the extremely smooth aerodynamic studies with which Sergio Pininfarina busied himself in the late '60s and early '70s, especially on Ferrari chassis. The same voluptuous contours were here, the same insistence on clean surfaces and excellent air penetration.

But there *was* a difference. All previous so-called "aerodynamic" bodies had a definite side, top, front,

Aerovette's near symmetry front-to-rear is readily apparent in profile.

Ultra-clean lines proved aerodynamically efficient.

Big 400-cid V-8 nestles under the Aerovette's large backlight.

and back. But the softened contours of the four-rotor car cleverly disguised where the edges began. There was hardly a straight line on it. The transitions from one surface area to another were never clearly delineated. From every angle the shape seemed organic, one-of-a-piece—right. As with any true work of art, moving any one plane would destroy the whole, so subtle was the surface detailing. Here was an aesthetic *tour de force,* a triumph of surface over line.

Vinnie Kay and Jerry Palmer were the stylists who actually sculpted the superb body for the XP-882 chassis. The finished car was first presented in Wankel form in late 1973, at which point *Car and Driver* magazine called it "the betting man's choice to replace the Stingray." But GM axed its Wankel as a result of the 1973-74 energy crisis, never to be revived.

But Bill Mitchell is nothing if not persistent. By 1977 Ed Cole was gone, and the four-rotor coupe was still sitting in the Special Vehicles warehouse, covered with a sheet. Like DeLorean before him, Mitchell had the car dragged out, and replaced the Wankel with the 400 cubic-inch small-block of the original XP-882. At this point, the car was dubbed "Aerovette," and Mitchell started lobbying at Chevrolet Division for it to be the next Corvette. As usual, if Mitchell wanted something badly enough, he got it, and GM chairman Thomas Murphy actually approved the Aerovette for the 1980 program. Ironically, that came about at least partly because of a possible threat from another, soon-to-be-announced sports car—the rear-engine DMC-12, an independent effort headed by none other than John Z. DeLorean.

By the end of 1977, Aerovette clays were complete, and tooling was scheduled to begin. So for a moment, at least, GM honestly intended to build the car. The production version was to have had the same gorgeous styling and a steel platform frame like that of the XP-882, complete with Duntov's clever transverse V-8. The production Corvette engine was a 350 by then, so that's probably the one that would have been used, though it could have been the 305 V-8 that wound up in California-bound 1980 versions of the existing Stingray. There would have been a choice of 4-speed manual or Turbo Hydra-matic transmissions. The suspension would have been pulled right off the Stingray, which, of course, was Duntov's original, cost-cutting goal. With a fiberglass body, gullwing doors, and fixed side windows, the Aerovette really wouldn't have been any more expensive to build than the Stingray. That would have meant a 1980 price tag in the $15,000-$18,000 range.

If any car would have been an instant classic the day it was released to public, the mid-engine Aerovette was it. Like the Stingray, it would almost certainly have been a 10-year-plus model, one that would have lasted up to 1990 in high style. It's a shame it never materialized. Even so, many of its design principles will figure in the actual replacement for the late-'60s model, due in two or three years. Thus, the legacy of Bill Mitchell will live on five years after his retirement from GM Styling.

Aerovette resembles current Stingray...a little.

Thrusting nose gives the car a look of motion even at rest.

Wheels and tires seem larger in this low-angle view.

Even nearly a decade later, it still looks "right."

On the Home Front:
Chrysler's Wartime Styling Studies

C hrysler products of the late '30s and early '40s were not revolutionary. But they were sound, and extremely well engineered. As a result, Chrysler Corporation made steady sales gains beginning in the depths of the Depression in 1932. By 1940, it was well ahead of Ford in production, and ranked second only to General Motors. Then came December 7, 1941, and the Japanese attack on Pearl Harbor. Civilian automobile production was halted for the duration of the war, and Chrysler built only a handful of cars in calendar year 1942 before shutting down its assembly lines in late February of that year.

During the war, Chrysler built a wide variety of defense equipment, and its output was astronomical. There were 120,000 anti-aircraft guns, over 18,000 nine-cylinder Wright Cyclone aircraft engines, 20,000 land-mine detectors, 2000 radar units, 1500 searchlight reflectors, 5500 Sperry Gyrocompasses (built under license), 7800 "Sea Mules" (utility harbor tugs), and 29,000 marine engines. In addition, Chrysler produced 25,000 tanks, of which 18,000 were Shermans. It was a proud record.

The ban on auto production was lifted fairly late in 1945, and Chrysler built only a few 1946 cars before year's end. But a semblance of normal production returned the following year. No one was in the least surprised that, like other prewar auto producers, Chrysler's '46 models were only mildly facelifted versions of their 1942 predecessors. In Chrysler's case, this was attributed to postwar material shortages and government controls, but the main reason was economic. Chrysler knew that for three, four, or possibly even five years after World War II, it could sell every car it could make, so it would be unnecessary to bring out anything new or different right away. And it would be financially foolish to scrap unamortized prewar dies simply for the sake of offering brand-new designs in 1947-48—unless you were Studebaker, which in retrospect probably should have saved its all-new '47s until 1949. So, like GM and Ford, Chrysler stood pat through 1948. It even extended its 1948 run through the first half of the 1949 model year.

"The plan was for each company to wring the profits out of its old models and stave off the rapidly rising cost of retooling, right up to the point where the law of diminishing returns began to operate," one former Chrysler insider noted. "[This was] the psychological point at which the buyer was beginning to make up his mind about the car he would purchase when he had a free choice. Before that point was reached, something new had to be added. But when? For each company the problem was slightly different."

None of this means that model revisions were not considered. Many ⅛- and ¼-scale clay models and hundreds of renderings had been devised for the 1943, 1944, and 1945 Chrysler Corporation products, which were well underway before the U.S. entered World War II. But interestingly, these ideas continued to be developed during the war years. Most evolved through lines set down by two prewar show cars, the Thunderbolt and Newport, the former designed by Alex Tremulis of Briggs, the latter by Ralph Roberts of LeBaron (a Briggs subsidiary by the late '30s).

"Styling at Briggs was almost a 'good will' department," said Tremulis, where Briggs "could offer our clients a fresh viewpoint free from engineering restrictions . . ." The Thunderbolt was a long, low retractable convertible—a two- or three-seater on a 127.5-inch-wheelbase Chrysler chassis. It featured a wrapped bright molding that formed a sort of perimeter bumper. The Newport, a dual-cowl phaeton on a 145.5-inch Imperial wheelbase, used a rakish envelope body with smoothly flowing fenders and soft lines. Ralph Roberts recalled that both these show cars were well liked by Chrysler president K. T. Keller: "K. T. liked to have outside talent around to encourage Chrysler's own designers, though he actually used very little of what we designed *in toto*. We eventually built six of each car."

Both Newport and Thunderbolt made the rounds of the car shows, where they were favorably received. At the same time, they influenced the line of Chrysler products that would have been seen in 1943-45 had not the war intervened.

Unlike the Newport/Thunderbolt, the wartime prototypes shown here were designed by Chrysler rather than Briggs. By the early '40s, an embryonic in-house styling department had been formed, directed by chief body engineer Oliver H. Clark, who reported to chief engineer Fred M. Zeder. Former coachbuilder Raymond H. Dietrich, who had directed Chrysler styling in the difficult post-Airflow period of the late '30s, had departed in 1938. Dietrich had been replaced by Robert Cadwallader, who directed the exterior design studios during 1943-45 model planning. (Cadwallader would leave Chrysler in 1946 to join the new Kaiser-Frazer firm, where he would briefly head the Kaiser design studio.) Chrysler's small styling unit copied GM by calling itself the Art & Colour Section. Despite its subservience to Engineering, the group possessed ample talent.

Two of its best designers were Arnott B. "Buzz" Grisinger and Herb Weissinger, who would later join Cadwallader at Kaiser-Frazer. Weissinger was a skilled artist and a clay model perfectionist. Tremulis called him "a maestro in the execution of a line on a surface. He regarded a ¹⁄₆₄-inch deviation in a roofline as unthinkable, and would work hours on end seeking its correction. His chrome appliqués were done with the perfection of a Cellini; he was easily the best of us in this area. He had the qualifications of a brilliant body engineer, and could cross swords with the best of them in the defense of Styling. After 40

This 1941 drawing for the '43 Dodge shows integral fenders.

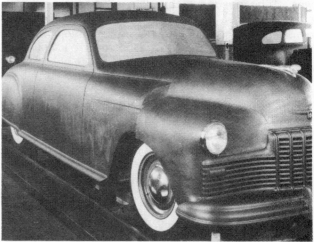
A more radical Dodge idea was fender-mounted air scoops.

DeSoto might have retained hidden lights in '43, as this front-end buck shows.

A less "toothy" DeSoto front displayed concave grille bars.

On the Home Front

years in the business, I feel qualified to judge those whom I consider best. Herb Weissinger was truly one of the greatest."

Grisinger, Tremulis said, was "the greatest sculptural design modeler of all time. Tremendously talented, he did very little on paper—usually a quick sketch. That was all he needed to attack a full-size clay model single-handedly. In his field he was in a class by himself. The body engineering draftsmen told me that they never had to surface-develop any irregularities in his models; they merely took templates off the clay and used his lines verbatim."

Chrysler's Art & Colour staff never exceeded several dozen, including clay modelers. During the war, it lost the services of many young men, including Grisinger (who was assigned to the Manhattan project, which developed the atomic bomb). Cadwallader and Weissinger remained, though, and can be credited with much of the stillborn 1943-45 designs—as well as the mildly facelifted '42 models that became Chrysler's production cars for 1946-48.

The 1943-45 proposals evolved from a design,

A Plymouth proposal from early 1940 shows how the postwar cars might have looked.

Stylists played with wraparound grillework and hidden headlights.

By mid-1942, Plymouth planning had progressed to this.

developed partly by Dietrich and partly by Cadwallader, that was introduced on Chrysler's 1940 lines. It was a sort of fat bathtub shape, with separate fenders at each corner and a massive grille with pointed horizontal bars. The grille sat between the headlights in 1940, but edged outward in 1941, and finally wrapped itself right around the forward part of the front fenders in 1942. The more expensive models were fitted with fender skirts bearing a shiny bauble where the hubcap would have been had the wheel had been visible—a remnant of the LeBaron days that had filtered down to Chrysler via Briggs. The Dietrich/Cadwallader design embodied separate fenders, though the 1943-45 proposals all featured integral fenderlines and more unified grilles.

The styling themes of Chrysler's wartime prototypes were uniform in that they weren't much different from make to make. While Plymouths, Dodges, DeSotos, and Chryslers all bore identifying medallions or script and were scaled to appropriate dimensions, it can be seen from the photographs here that they were a closely related family.

The 1940s were the years of "second-generation streamlining." Styling had progressed past the rounded fenders and teardrop body shapes of the initial mid-'30s era. Now, the look was beoming more "organic": headlights were disappearing into fenders, free-standing bumpers were moving closer to the body, wheel wells were being covered by skirts. Chrysler's wartime work followed these trends, with integral fenders (which did not appear in production form until 1955), wraparound bumpers and side moldings, and wrapped windshields and backlights. The glass industry's technology in those days didn't allow for much curvature, which is why the wraparound windows on these styling models would not be practical for another decade. Up front, the designers tried to combine various components as a complicated, chromey grille. More expensive models have hidden headlights, while on others the headlamps are part of the basic grille shape. There are a few hood scoops in evidence; most of the cars here carry clean hoods, lacking even an ornament. (The clean-hood idea—to the horror of salesmen—was reflected in the 1947 K-F cars finalized by Grisinger, Weissinger, and Cadwallader.)

Chrysler continued its design experiments sporadically throughout the war years. Their influence can be seen in the '46 facelifts. The busy front end seen on one wartime Imperial proposal, for example, worked its way into the 1946-48 Chrysler grille. The pointed horizontal-bar grille of one Plymouth was closely matched in postwar production. And DeSoto's trademark "teeth" really emerged from the design work of 1943-45. But there were some elements that would never be seen in production. Hidden headlights, which had made a brief appearance on the '42 DeSoto, were written off after the war as unnecessary and expensive. Fender skirts, especially for the front wheels, were thought to be taking streamlining too far. Thin upper window frames (which very much resemble those of the production 1949-51 Lincoln and 1952-57 Nash) were abandoned, too. They would have required expensive plated metal or extruded aluminum; it was much less costly to build window frames in the old, heavy-handed way.

Though these wartime styling studies were examined when Chrysler began planning its first all-new postwar cars for 1949, they actually contributed very little to that program. For one thing, they were obsolete by then. The industry was moving away from bulky, rounded styling—if not in current 1948-49 products, then at least for those to come in the early '50s. And K. T. Keller, who was adamant about the need for adequate headroom, wanted boxy, upright cars rather than streamlined torpedos. This is exactly what he got in the 1949 line.

Ironically, Keller's boxy '49s were far more efficient in use of space and raw materials than these 1943-45 prototypes; yet the wartime designs probably would have sold better. The public resisted the "boxes" in increasing numbers after about 1950, and Ford passed Chrysler in volume by 1952. Chrysler styling, which had been the industry's most practical in 1949-54, became flashy but handsome for 1955-56. The 1957 models ushered in the age of tailfins. After that, things would never be the same for the styling department— or the company itself.

Later that same year, a peaked grille and two-toning were tried.

Grille on this wartime Plymouth model is close to the '46.

Odd headlamp shape was used on this '41 proposal, probably a Chrysler.

Wraparound side trim and bumpers were favorite wartime styling themes.

This 1942 fastback sedan is somewhat Ford-like.

Ford and Chrysler worked with similar ideas, as on this 1942 model.

Complex grille marks this design as a Chrysler. Note upper "nostrils."

"Pregnant" wheel wells of this model probably wouldn't have been popular.

Chrysler's Stillborn Sports Cars:
Excitement From Exner

The name Virgil Exner never became what you'd call a household word. But in the '50s, it was probably on the lips of more car enthusiasts than that of any other auto stylist.

Exner's design career had begun with GM in 1930, when he managed Pontiac styling and created the famous "Silver Streak" trim motif. In 1938, he joined the Raymond Loewy organization at South Bend, and helped develop Studebaker's life-saving 1939 Champion. After the war, he left Loewy and became a freelancer, competing against his former boss for Studebaker assignments. Then, in mid-1949, he joined Chrysler, and on the strength of his efforts rose to become that firm's styling chief by the mid-'50s.

Exner is perhaps best remembered as the creator of the 1955 Chrysler Corporation line—which turned the company's red ink to black, and brought excitement into its showrooms for the first time in two decades. But his influence at Chrysler was apparent much earlier than that. Working with Carrozzeria Ghia in Italy, he created several sports and sporting cars, beginning in 1950 with the Plymouth XX-500, and evolving through the fabulous XNR of 1960. It is not widely known that several of these exercises came within a hair of mass production as Chrysler's answer to the Corvette and Thunderbird.

Chrysler K-310, 1951

This dashing hardtop coupe was designed in secret in Detroit. The resulting 3/8-scale clay plaster was then shipped to Ghia to guide construction of a full-size running prototype. The "K" stood for Chrysler president K. T. Keller, the 310 for the alleged horsepower of its big 331-cid hemi engine—though the stock version at that time delivered only 180 bhp. But whatever its horsepower, the K-310 was an immediate sensation.

As Chrysler put it, this car was conceived as "a whole unit. The theme [was] a single one, to which all components [were] intimately related. Concentration on various parts such as fenders, top, front end, etc. [was] not possible until the overall picture [was] clearly established." To distinguish the K-310 from its slab-sided contemporaries a "hitch" was designed into its front fenders, emphasizing the rounded front end. Full fender cut-outs accentuated the wheels, which Exner rarely covered on any of his cars. "The wheel," he said, "is one of man's oldest and most vital inventions. Why attempt to hide it?" Subtle two-toning integrated the upper and lower body structure, while the rear fenders continued the rounded theme. The roof and deck were proportioned to accentuate the long hood—not easy

Unlike most Italian customs, the K-310's body was done in steel, not aluminum. "Aluminum was so fragile," Exner said, "we didn't think it would hold up. Even [with steel], the K-310 only cost $20,000 to build on a stock production chassis. But everything on the body was completely new and there were no production parts used on it whatsoever."

The K-310 and a 1952 soft-top successor, the C-200, were both strongly considered for production. Keller, said Exner, "liked it and thought it was something they should promote . . . It was quite well received by the public, too. Of course, it was also something into which they could put their hemi engine. It was a perfect combination."

In the end, though, the K-310 proved to be a car-that-never-was for the most basic of reasons: money. Chrysler sales started to plunge in the early '50s, and by 1952 the company was being outproduced by Ford for the first time since the mid-'30s. Plans for a limited run of "street" K-310s were accordingly shelved—but Exner didn't stop campaigning for a Chrysler Corporation sports car.

DeSoto Adventurer I, 1954

In the early '50s, Ghia had produced about 400 examples of another Chrysler special called the GS-1. Then the Corvette appeared in 1953, and Exner again tried to interest management in a sports model. In 1954, he brought out the pretty DeSoto Adventurer, stylistically related to the K-310 but on a more appropriate 111-inch wheelbase, created by shortening a stock DeSoto chassis. Since most of its length was between the wheels, the Adventurer could comfortably accommodate four passengers. Its off-white coupe body was decorated with outside exhaust pipes, a quick-fill racing-type fuel tank cap, and wire wheels. The interior was upholstered in black leather, and the satin-finished aluminum dash held a complete complement of circular gauges.

Exner admitted he tried very hard to make the

considering the long (stock Saratoga) 125.5-inch wheelbase.

The K-310 introduced several design touches that later appeared on production Chryslers. The seats were divided 1/3-2/3, the door handles were flush, and there was an eggcrate grille. A spare tire deck imprint decorated the rear, along with distinctive "gunsight" taillights, later transferred almost without change to the 1955 Imperial.

Swanky K-310 show car introduced gunsight taillights and embossed trunklid motif later seen on Imperial.

The DeSoto Adventurer was the second of Exner's sporty two-seaters, and his personal favorite of the Ghia-built prototypes.

Chrysler's Stillborn Sports Cars

Adventurer a limited-production model. But as Maury Baldwin, one of his stylists, remembered: "Management at that point was very stodgy. A lot of people attributed it to the old Airflow disaster. They were afraid to make any new inroads." Baldwin's boss later said that the Adventurer came closer to production than any other Chrysler special up to that time: "If it had been built, it would have been the first four-passenger sports car made in this country. It was better than a two-plus-two. Of course, it had a DeSoto hemi. It was my favorite car always, and I owned it for three years and kept it at home. I don't know what became of it—I think it eventually went to a wealthy collector in South America." (A second DeSoto special, the 1955 Adventurer II, was primarily a Ghia design and was not actively considered for production.)

Chrysler Falcon, 1955

By the time the two-seat Falcon was shown, Ford had previewed its '55 Thunderbird and Chrysler's sales were recovering, so a Mopar sports car seemed quite

Adventurer's interior was very businesslike. Seatbacks were very slim for the early '50s.

Handsome rather than pretty, the Adventurer almost made it to the showrooms.

Ghia followed up with this 1955 DeSoto special.

Odd roof may be the reason Adventurer II never made it.

logical. In fact, Chrysler built three copies of the Falcon, all on a special 105-inch wheelbase comparable to the 102 inches of the Corvette and Thunderbird. Styled mainly by Maury Baldwin, the Falcon was a truly handsome design that still looks good today. But a limited market and the '58 recession are the likely reasons it never saw an assembly line.

Incidentally, the Falcon name came close to being used for Chrysler's 1960 compact (instead of Valiant), but Ford talked the company out of it. "I remember Dad talking about Ford wanting the name," Virgil Exner, Jr. noted. "It was kind of hard to let go, but he agreed. There was no money involved, just a kind of 'return favor' sort of deal. It's ironic that the name he chose survived longer than either 'Corvair' or 'Valiant.' "

The Chrysler Falcon used a 170-bhp DeSoto hemi V-8 that displaced 276.1 cubic inches. The transmission was PowerFlite two-speed automatic, controlled— none too positively—by a wispy floor-mounted wand. The body and frame were of integral steel construction, and curb weight was a hefty 3300 pounds. But performance was perfectly adequate. In a brief road test of the only known surviving Falcon, one of the contributors to this book found that 0-60 took 10 seconds flat, and top speed was about 115 mph. The car ran the standing-start quarter mile in 17.5 seconds at 82.0 mph—more than impressive in 1955. Fuel mileage averaged around 15 mpg.

Despite its weight, the Falcon had a beautifully balanced chassis, with an ease and precision of steering totally lacking in most American cars of the era. The only real problem was lack of headroom due

1955 Falcon had impressive performance and beautiful handling.

to a very low windshield, though this would have been corrected in production.

In design, the Falcon was, in the advertising vernacular of the day, "Poetry in Motion." It was lithe, nimble-looking, perfect from every angle. Certainly, it would have been a strong competitor to the Corvette and Thunderbird. In character, it was probably the best combination of refinement and performance among the three.

Plymouth XNR, 1960

The most radical and interesting Exner special, the Plymouth XNR (the reference in the initials is obvious) represented its designer's peak of enthusiasm as head of Chrysler styling. With its unique and imaginative "Asymmetrical Styling," it stood out boldly, to say the

Chrysler built three copies of the Falcon. Top hid under a metal cover behind the seats. It's still a good-looking car.

Chrysler's Stillborn Sports Cars

least. The idea here was to emphasize the off-center driver's position, as many racing cars did. A prominent hood scoop was faired into the cowl, topped by a squat, racer-style windscreen. The line was carried rearward through a combination headrest-and-tailfin behind the driver. The XNR's combination bumper/grille, also fairly advanced for the time, formed a large oval containing a mesh grille and quad headlights. The passenger seat was covered by a metal tonneau when not in use. When occupied, a small fold-flat auxiliary windshield could be popped up.

According to Chrysler, the asymmetrical hood scoop/headrest/fin was created "because the driver's head and shoulders would project into the wind on such a low car." But Virgil Exner held that this was the first design to emphasize the real focus of the automobile—namely, driving.

This breaktaking Plymouth rode a 106-inch wheelbase, was 195 inches long, and measured 43 inches from ground to the top if its rear fin. Power came from the hairiest version of the Valiant's 225-cid slant six ever developed: 250 horsepower—1.11 bhp per cubic inch. "We took it to the proving grounds and had a professional drive it," said Exner. "He lapped at 151 or 152, which wasn't bad for that time." That isn't bad

anytime. What excited sports car fans—and led to rumors of its impending production—was the efficient, economical nature of the beast. The XNR had the first performance six from Chrysler, and the second high-output postwar American six after the Hudson Hornet. It would have been an ideal sports car, and capable of racing against any competition in its displacement class.

Unfortunately, Chrysler decided the XNR was too radical to build in the small quantities that would have been warranted by the size of the contemporary sports car market. And with Exner's departure from the corporation in 1961, the XNR had little chance of being refined into a more practical version suitable for production. A derivation, the Valiant Assimetrica, was later built by Ghia, but it had none of the XNR's flair and never evolved beyond the one-off stage.

The fabulous XNR still exists, though its whereabouts are hard to document. It was last seen in the pages of *National Geographic,* being enthusiastically driven by (appropriately enough) a Kuwaiti sheik.

It's unfortunate that none of Chrysler's exciting sports car prototypes emerged as a product the public could buy. One look at the light, sleek K-310, the lovely Adventurer, the beautifully balanced Falcon, or the wild XNR, and it's easy to imagine how pleasing they would have been in production form. Happily, a few of these experimentals have survived, and more may come to light in future years. Long after his death, they remain among the best examples of Virgil Exner's inimitable styling legacy.

XNR reflected Exner's interest in asymmetrical styling.

Underneath the XNR's racy sheetmetal beat the heart of a Valiant.

Low-cut racing windscreen topped bulging hood scoop. Line was continued rearward by the finned headrest fairing.

Turbine Tale:
25 years of Experimental Chryslers

Chrysler's interest in gas turbines dates to before World War II, but it wasn't until after the war that it built a turbo-prop aircraft engine for the Navy Bureau of Aeronautics. It was only in the early '50s that the company began seriously considering a gas-turbine automobile.

The turbine engine is not a complex design, but it presents problems when it comes to production feasibility. Its main element, of course, is a turbine wheel with a ring of blades around its circumference. A mixture of fuel and air flows past the blades, causing the wheel to rotate and produce power. The turbine engine is at its best at constant rpm, so it's ideal for aircraft, which usually fly at steady speeds. But a car must be able to change speed, so its engine must be able to give good acceleration and engine braking as well as smooth constant-speed cruising. Also, differences in vehicle design and use conditions mean a turbine would have to run quieter and cooler in a car than in a plane. And today's government standards require minimal exhaust emissions—the main reason Chrysler has not continued turbine development in recent years.

For its automobile turbine engine, Chrysler's engineers developed a rotating heat exchanger, or regenerator. The exchanger recovered heat from exhaust gases, kept running temperatures reasonably low, and made fuel mileage more acceptable than it would be otherwise. In short, it made the turbine engine much more practical for automotive use. Problems of operating flexibility and development of alloys able to withstand a turbine's tremendous heat were also investigated early on. Engine tests began in 1954 with a stock-looking Plymouth Belvedere hardtop.

The '54 turbine engine, rated at 100 bhp, was successfully tested at Chrysler's Chelsea, Michigan proving grounds, but only a single test car was built. A later version based on a 1956 Belvedere sedan was driven cross-country in a test of durability and performance. The car performed satisfactorily, but recorded only 13 miles per gallon, which was excessive even then. Both these cars were powered by the "first-generation" Chrysler turbine. Compared to the cars that followed, they were extremely expensive to build.

A "second-generation" engine was first seen in a 1959 Plymouth hardtop on a run from Detroit to New York. This turbine produced about 200 bhp, used new materials for some internal parts, and was more efficient than the earlier version. Metallurgical research had, by now, produced relatively inexpensive heat- and oxidation-resistant alloys for engine construction.

"Third-generation" turbine engines were installed in three different vehicles: a stock-looking 1960 Plymouth, a 2.5-ton Dodge truck, and a unique show car designed by Maury Baldwin called the TurboFlite. "I think this was the last 'Virgil Exner' show car," Baldwin said. "We incorporated a lot of interesting things in it. Entrance-wise, the whole cockpit above the beltline lifted to admit passengers. Mounted between the fins was a deceleration flap, such as now used on racing cars. The headlights were retractable. The car was built by Ghia—we did a ⅜-scale model and then full-size drawings. It was probably one of the best engineered show cars we ever did."

By 1962, Chrysler had developed its CR2A gas turbine, first fitted to a four-door hardtop Dodge Dart, which traveled from New York to Los Angeles on yet another endurance run. The Dart scored better fuel economy than a conventionally powered "control" car traveling with it. A turbine-powered '62 Plymouth Fury two-door hardtop was also built. The CR2A differed from earlier turbines by the addition of a variable fuel nozzle mechanism, which provided engine braking and better performance. By varying the angle of the jet stream to the turbine blades on take-off, acceleration was strongly improved. The nozzles eliminated most of the throttle lag that had plagued earlier turbines. While

Chrysler engineer puts "Turbine Special" badge to this modified 1956 Plymouth.

1962 Turbo Dart ran coast-to-coast to prove reliability of CR2A turbine.

1961 TurboFlite show car was powered by Chrysler's third-generation turbine.

Cockpit canopy and rear deceleration flap were two of TurboFlite's unique features.

Turbine Tale

the first-generation engines had taken 7.0 seconds to go from idle to full power output, the CR2A needed only 1.5-2.0 seconds. Pleased by the improvement, Chrysler decided to build 50-75 turbine-powered passenger cars for consumer evaluation starting in 1963.

The result was the most famous Chrysler turbine car of all, expressly designed for this program by Virgil Exner's replacement at Styling, Elwood Engel. Engel had come over from Ford after working on the 1961-63 Thunderbird. Not surprisingly, the turbine car, first displayed in May 1963, bore a striking resemblance to his T-Bird. But if anything, it was more beautiful. All these turbine prototypes were bucket-seated, four-passenger, two-door hardtops, and all were painted bronze. Power steering, brakes, and window lifts; automatic transmission; and other luxury equipment were included. Headlight and backup light bezels were done in a rotary-blade motif to emphasize the special powerplant. Horizontal taillights were set into steeply angled rear fenders.

Under the hood was the latest "fourth-generation" gas turbine with twin regenerators that rotated in vertical planes, one on each side, with a centrally controlled burner. It was quieter, lighter, and less bulky than the CR2A. Acceleration lag was reduced to 1.0-1.5 seconds. Maximum-output engine speed after gear reduction was 4680 rpm, compared to the CR2A's 5360 rpm, and the new engine had 20 percent fewer moving parts than a conventional piston powerplant. While the new turbine's horsepower was down slightly compared to its predecessor; torque was up from 375 to 425 foot-pounds.

Because of the limited number, the 50 turbine cars were built by Ghia in Italy. They were sent out to

"consumer representatives" chosen from over 30,000 inquiries received after the announcement that the public would participate in turbine testing. Each driver had the use of the car for about three months. All 48 contiguous states were included in the field test, with "owners" ranging in age from 21 to 70. In all, 203 persons drove the Ghia-built turbine cars between 1963 and early 1966.

The report on the testing program, issued in 1967, noted that the turbine required little or no maintenance compared with a piston engine. But Chrysler never divulged fuel mileage, which, apparently, was embarrassing. One out of four drivers complained about gas guzzling, despite the fact that the cars would also run on kerosene, jet fuel, unleaded gas, or diesel fuel. One out of three disliked the acceleration lag, while the main compliments centered around the car's vibration-less operation and the snazzy styling.

Chrysler never released one of the bronze hardtops to a car magazine, though writer John Lawlor managed to land one surreptitiously toward the end of the public-evaluation campaign. Lawlor was impressed with the turbine's smoothness, but was disconcerted by the lack of available engine braking and by the acceleration lag, which he calculated at the specified 1.0-1.5 seconds. Fuel mileage was also disappointing—11.5 mpg—though the fuel used was usually cheap kerosene. Lawlor did comment on the car's sparkling acceleration, averaging less than 10 seconds for the 0-60 mph sprint. This put to rest the rumors that turbine cars weren't fast.

Writing in a magazine about Plymouth, Dodge, and Chrysler in 1973, Lawlor commented in retrospect about his experience: "Getting 11.5 mpg out of a 4100-pound car that can go from zero to 60 in 11 seconds has begun to look like an attractive proposition, particularly when you consider that the fuel used could be a much cheaper one than today's gasoline." One wonders if he wouldn't have changed his mind a year later in the wake of the Arab oil embargo. While the turbine can run on almost any kind of fuel, diesel was hard to come by along many highways even then. Kerosene is still mainly sold in expensive gallon cans at hardware stores.

Today, of course, with gasoline at a premium and diesel fuel both cheaper and more widely available, Chrysler's turbine engine could again be very attractive. Considering the amount of weight cutting and downsizing that has gone on since the early '60s (and continues to go on as we move through the 1980s), it is not hard to imagine the same kind of engine powering a more efficiently designed automobile at close to 20 mpg—on diesel fuel. Had the turbine become a common means of motive propulsion, we might have even seen the return of the old-time kerosene pump at many service stations.

But Chrysler's interest in the turbine waned. The advent of emission standards, followed by corporate average fuel economy (CAFE) requirements and the firm's sagging financial fortunes, certainly put a wet blanket on the turbine for automotive use. Yet the

Styled by Elwood Engel, the 1963 turbine car was built by Ghia. Only 50 were made—all for "consumer evaluation."

Rear end styling was most distinctive part of the turbine car's design.

Headlamp bezels had "blades" to suggest the car's unusual powerplant.

Relatively few of these survive. Most had to be torched to avoid import duty.

Chrysler's most recent turbine car is this 1977 LeBaron-based special.

question persists: should we have explored the idea further? Somebody at Chrysler must have thought so, because turbine development has not stopped completely.

In 1970, Chrysler's research director, George J. Huebner, approached the Department of Transportation with an analysis of alternate power sources— electric, steam, and the then sixth-generation Chrysler gas turbine. Predictably, Huebner proved the turbine a better alternative than either of its rivals. Its road behavior had been much improved by then. Throttle lag and fuel consumption had been reduced from 1966 levels. While high manufacturing costs and exhaust emissions levels still posed nagging problems, Huebner suggested they could be licked with an ample dose of federal cash.

In late 1972, the newly created Environmental Protection Agency awarded Chrysler a small $6.4 million contract to investigate the cost and emission problems of the turbine. The company continues its research to this day. Perhaps the turbine will surface once again with a better chance for mass production than ever before. Certainly modern technology can solve a lot of the problems that beset it in the '60s. And certain characteristics of the gas turbine, like throttle

lag, may be things drivers can get used to.

What happened to the Ghia-built turbine experimental cars? We're sorry you asked. All but 10 were cut up with torches before the watchful eyes of United States Customs. Since they had been manufactured abroad, they were allowed to be imported duty-free, but only for testing purposes. Once that program ended, Chrysler would have had to return them to Italy or pay a considerable amount of cash for the then-dubious pleasure of keeping them on an American road. For the sake of history, Chrysler did cough up enough money to pay the duty on 10 of them. Eight were dispersed to museums such as Harrah's in Reno, Nevada, and Chicago's Museum of Science and Industry. The company kept only two, which were sent to the garages at its Chelsea proving grounds, and are probably there yet.

But, to quote the title of this book, the Chrysler turbines were cars that never were. They are an unfortunately forgotten piece of automotive technology, but one that may be only temporarily neglected. Continued doubts about the long-range future of the traditional internal-combustion piston engine could well mean that—in cars at least—the turbine will make a comeback.

Continental Mark II:
What Might Have Happened For '58

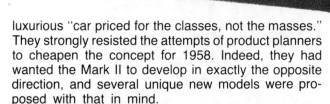

The Continental Mark II was never officially a Lincoln. But it is one of the most famous postwar cars of all—one of the first true collectables recognized by restorers and enthusiasts. With its dignified, almost classic, lines, the Mark II shunned the styling fads of its era. It ranks with the Studebaker Starliner and Ford's first Thunderbird as a leading design achievement of the 1950s. Luxuriously finished inside and out, the Mark IIs were powered by specially selected and balanced Lincoln 368-cid V-8s, which produced 285 bhp in 1956 and 300 bhp in 1957.

Initially only one Mark II model was offered—a close-coupled hardtop coupe listing at $10,000, but more often sold for well under that. In fact, Ford lost about $1000 on every Mark II because this was primarily an "image" car, a line leader—more of an ego trip than a calculated profitmaker. This led to its 1958 replacement, a line of less distinctive Mark III models based on that year's Lincoln platform and priced at around $6000. But that wasn't the way things were planned.

The Mark II design had stemmed from Ford's Special Products Division (which later became Continental Division) under William Clay Ford, the younger brother of Henry Ford II. The stylists were John Reinhart (formerly of Packard), Gordon Buehrig (the famed designer of the Cord 810), and Robert Thomas, with consultation provided by the great coachbuilder Raymond H. Dietrich. The Mark II's special "cow-belly" chassis was conceived by a brilliant engineer, Harley F. Copp. Together with W. C. Ford, these men were firmly committed to the concept of an elegant and luxurious "car priced for the classes, not the masses." They strongly resisted the attempts of product planners to cheapen the concept for 1958. Indeed, they had wanted the Mark II to develop in exactly the opposite direction, and several unique new models were proposed with that in mind.

The original program for the 1958 Continental envisioned an unchanged Mark II coupe. "It was so perfect a design," said John Reinhart, "that we felt it could go as long as ten years. But that was before somebody decided that the Continental would have to be a profit builder—which was a perfectly understandable, but discouraging, decision."

In addition to the coupe, the '58 line probably would have included a limousine-type vehicle designed to be chauffeur-driven. Gordon Buehrig saw this as an opportunity to resurrect one of his 1930s styles, and used the term "berline" (it means sedan in French) for this long and roomy Continental.

Though proposals for the berline were numerous and took many directions, what emerged was not unlike the production 1958 Mark III sedan—but subtly different. The berline carried a slightly higher, Mark II-like, fine-mesh grille. Since quad headlights had been ordained for 1958, it had these, too, but the lower light in each vertical "stack" was encased in the front bumper, instead of being above it as on the production Mark III. This visually separated it from the

From the A-pillar forward, the Berline was similar to the actual '58 styling. Headlamps were vertically stacked, however, not canted.

upper (low beam) headlamp, and retained a family resemblance to the Mark II. The sides of the car were smooth, with no chrome decoration except on the rocker panel. A body crease resembling that of the Mark II was the only interruption in the berline's clean form. The roof, though much longer than the coupe's, took the same "formal" shape at the rear. The deck was also like the Mark II's with a spare tire bulge built in at a rakish angle.

The other proposal for 1958 was a retractable-hardtop convertible. Contrary to popular opinion, this was *not* inspired by the '57 Ford Skyliner. In fact, it was just the opposite.

The retractable idea first came about in 1954 at Special Products Division, where it was projected for the '58 Continental line. Only after it was decided to come out with the cheaper Lincoln-based Mark III was the retractable transferred to Ford. According to John Reinhart, "we modeled the 1957 Ford Skyliner using techniques developed from the Mark II . . . The retrac had many different [electrical] sequences which activated the top, lifted the rear deck, and tucked it under. It was a fantastically hard job for the engineers because they had to break and hinge the roof." Reinhart noted that in Lincoln's 1961 four-door convertibles there was more room for the soft top to disappear, "thanks to a very long deck."

Reinhart continued: ". . . with the two-door, the retrac, and the berline, we felt we had a full line of cars. And we thought that each one would be a 'classic' in its own right. But we got stopped at the gate." What happened is a familiar story to most Mark II enthusiasts: Ford brought in a Mercury production expert, and the 1958 Mark III was downgraded far below the Mark II. Its lower price and build costs naturally permitted more production volume, and the Mark III made a profit for the first time in Continental's postwar history.

To be chronologically accurate, the proposed Mark II berline and retractable were not immediately shelved after management's review. There was a lapse of six months before the final decision was made to "Mer-

curyize" the Continental. During that time, management considered holding with the Mark II coupe as the only model for awhile to see what sales would be like. The berline and retractable were gradually sidetracked.

While this evaluation was going on, Continental Division ordered a custom soft-top convertible built as a present for Mrs. W. C. Ford. Constructed by the Derham Company of Rosemont, Pennsylvania, it had a soft top with "formal" (blind) rear quarters in the style of the production Mark II hardtop. Later, another convertible was cobbled out of a Mark II coupe by a private party in Florida. Both these cars still exist, and testify that an open Mark II would have been impressive in soft-top or retractable form. But there was never a move to put the soft-top into production, either.

For enthusiasts, the 1958-60 Mark III/IV/V Continentals are considerably less appealing than the more individual Mark II of 1956-57. Ford, however, was delighted with the change. The later Marks rode a huge 131-inch wheelbase, and met customer demand of the day with elongated fenders, garish chrome appliqués, canted tailfins, and diagonally stacked quad headlamps. What's more, they were available in four body styles: sedan, two- and four-door hardtops, and a convertible. The '59 Mark IV line added a town car and limousine, which accomplished what the proposed Mark II berline was aiming for at considerably less cost. The Mark V of 1960 retained the same six-model lineup.

The Marks then temporarily ended, replaced by the 1961 Lincoln Continental four-door hardtop and four-door convertible. Continental Division quietly disappeared as a separate entity, fading back into a reformed Lincoln-Mercury Division following the demise of Edsel and the MEL—Mercury-Edsel-Lincoln—structure. Continental was revived as a distinct make with the Mark III coupe of 1968 (the name was used on Lincoln models from 1961 to '67). But never again was there consideration of anything as exotic as the unborn Mark II berline or retractable—two more cars that unfortunately never made it to the showrooms.

Davis:
Three Wheels Weren't Enough

The three-wheeled Davis, like almost all the other new nameplates that appeared after World War II, was a flop. All the cars that eventually became postwar orphans had promised bright, assured futures. But unlike some of the others, the Davis never left the starting line. Inventor Gary Davis constructed enough parts to build 100 running prototypes, and at one point 17 were actually out on road tests. Far fewer than the planned 100 were actually built.

In late 1970, Gary Davis was interviewed by Michael Lamm, then editor of *Special-Interest Autos* magazine. This account is based on that interview, in which Davis was candid and outspoken about his experience. The car in the photograph belongs to Roy Davis (no relation), who bought it mainly because he wanted a car with his name on it. In place of its original four-cylinder engine, Roy Davis' Davis runs a Nash six.

At one point during the photo session, Roy was asked to turn the single front wheel sharply so the car's cornering behavior could be shown. When he did so, at no more than 15 mph, the right rear wheel lifted about two feet off the ground, the car bicycled precariously for a second or two, then skittered along on its aluminum nose. Luckily, it landed back on all three wheels, and was little the worse for wear.

This "interesting" handling aside, the Davis was a novel package. The slippery design was the work of a group of aircraft engineers whom Gary Davis had recruited. The body was made of aluminum for light weight, and combined with the smooth shape for good performance. The 60-bhp Hercules side-valve four displaced only 133 cubic inches. Yet, Davis claimed that it would see the car to 100 mph, and return as much as 35 mpg when driven at more moderate speeds. Unique, too, were the standard front disc brakes, though they were of the clutch-type rather than caliper. The 108-inch wheelbase provided room for up to five passengers in comfort. Davis hoped to sell the car for $1400—rather a lot in 1949, as a conventional Chevy or Ford cost about as much. But failure to produce, followed by a lawsuit against the builder, which led to his 18-month incarceration, make the Davis three-wheeler just another footnote in history.

Davis himself used to do U-turns at 55 mph to demonstrate the car's handling abilities—somewhat surprising after watching Roy Davis' car lose itself at only 15 mph. But Davis admitted he had a certain edge: "Part of [my U-turn act] was being so familiar—loving the car so much that I was part of it. And nobody else could ever do it but me . . . I knew how to balance my weight . . . Now one thing about this particular [Roy Davis'] car: it has a Nash Statesman engine in it, and that throws off the weight factor. [The original four weighed] 486 pounds. You can't put an 800- or 900-pound engine in there and expect it to work .

Davis was next asked about design details. "Pete Lansberg, who'd been in charge of the DC-6 landing gear, evolved the front suspension so it would last a lifetime. [The body] design was a 'configuration' and not really a design at all. It had the least resistance to drag . . . a wraparound deal. I wrapped the configuration of the sheetmetal in the easiest possible way. The main idea was that each one of these panels could be put on with Dzus fasteners. And yet the car looks as fresh, undated today as it did 22 years ago.

Davis was obviously as enthusiastic about his car in 1970 as he was in 1949. Yet, he was equally willing to talk about the legal troubles that killed it. "I sold franchises, and all I gave [the dealers] was the right to sell the Davis car. [But] the contract that they signed was completely ignored." Six dealers testified that Davis had promised to deliver cars in 30 days—in spite of the contract—in oral conversation at the Davis Company offices. Gary Davis felt this was a trumped-up charge: "I didn't even know these people and I never said that. I, being a realist, knew it would take 18 months at least to get [a car] into production."

The convicted Davis was not sentenced to state prison. Instead, he went to a "misdemeanor farm" for 18 months. Afterward, he was given probation, on the stipulation he wouldn't get back in the car business. That always amused him, Davis said, because if he had really been a fraud, he would have never built a car in the first place!

With heavy, non-stock Nash engine, Davis was tippy in turns.

The Last DeSoto:

It Would Have Been New in '62

On November 18, 1960, in a terse 165-word statement, Chrysler Corporation announced the death of the DeSoto after 32 mostly successful years. The end came a little more than a month after introduction of the 1961 models. Advertising billboards were taken down, and the DeSoto exhibit at the Pittsburgh Automobile Show was closed the day of the announcement. A paltry 3034 of the last models were assembled. Yet as recently as 1957, DeSoto production had topped 125,000 units.

Tucked away in the styling studios at Highland Park was a never-to-be-seen 1962 DeSoto. It was to be a brand-new car embodying a radical new styling philosophy. In fact, all of Chrysler's 1962 full-size or S-series cars were to be completely redesigned—DeSoto included. Of these, only the Dodge and Plymouth versions saw the light of day.

For the first time since 1955, DeSoto was to be shorn of its famous fins. In their place was to be an all-new look based on the XNR show car, then in preparation (see Chapter 6), created by styling vice-president Virgil Exner. His long-hood/short-deck approach was set to appear first on the 1960 Valiant. The first clays for the new S-series cars took shape in late 1958 in the secrecy of Exner's "back room" studio, where specially selected stylists and modelers could work on advanced concepts free from the pressures and deadlines of the production studios.

After initial exploratory work using ⅜-scale models, a full-size "theme" clay (a convertible) was completed and wheeled into the styling showroom in May 1959. It was radically different from previous Chrysler products because of its dramatically altered proportions. Its passenger compartment was further rearward than usual to emphasize hood length, while the rear deck was truncated, a 180-degree swing from the long-tailed

Pontiac Bonnevilles and Olds 98s of the period. The long hood signaled a reversal in design direction. Exner's finned fantasies had made Chrysler the industry's styling leader since 1955. But fins were becoming dated by the late '50s, and Exner was searching for the next "Forward Look." The tailfins had emphasized the rear of the car. Now, in a literal turnaround, the front was to be visually more important, harking back to the 1930s when hood length was the recognized expression of power and style.

Other unusual characteristics of that May mock-up included V-shaped front and rear bumpers, a beltline notched up over the rear wheels, and vestigial fins (which were soon abandoned). Also featured was curved side glass, which had first appeared on the 1957 Imperial, and extensive bodyside sculpturing. The base of the windshield was pulled forward at the center line for a sports car look.

In addition to the long hood, the front end was further highlighted by a long horizontal fender blade lifted from the XNR. It ran back from the headlights and stopped abruptly two-thirds of the way into the front door. On the rear quarter panel, a sculptured horizontal rectangle began beneath the notched belt, and flowed aft into the deck.

This mockup had a great impact on management compared with competing S-series clays from the production studios. After approving Exner's theme model, management instructed the individual car-line studios to develop their 1962 designs around this base. Since both Chrysler and DeSoto would share body-shells and basic sheetmetal (as in the past), Don Kopka, who headed the DeSoto studio, had to work closely with his Chrysler counterpart, Fred Reynolds.

For both cars, the theme clay's rear-quarter sculpturing was soon modified in side view to complement the

The Last DeSoto

tapering rear deck. The result was quickly dubbed the "chicken wing" by junior stylists. As the cars evolved, both front and rear bumpers acquired dropped center sections. At the time, Exner was experimenting with various shapes, as evidenced on the 1960 Imperial and Plymouth, to replace traditional straight bumper bars. The rear of the developing DeSoto heralded a return to the triple-taillight treatment of 1956-59, though the taillights were mounted horizontally rather than vertically. By contrast, Chryslers were slated for wraparound taillights visible from the sides.

The front end on both cars featured four headlights, each mounted in individual chromed bezels and arranged in vee'd pairs as on the '61 DeSoto and Chrysler. Above the grille on both was a molding that flowed over the hood and back into the belt molding. This was the longest continuous molding on the cars, again for front-end emphasis, and there were no front-to-back bodyside moldings. DeSoto stylists played with a variety of grille treatments, finally choosing a rather undistinguished blend of thick and thin horizontal bars with a center emblem for accent. Chrysler stuck with the inverted trapezoid it had introduced in 1961. The grille design for the 300 preserved that model's traditional crossed-bars motif.

As different from their finned predecessors as the DeSoto and Chrysler were, the proposed S-series Imperial diverged even more. Its front end was an evolution of the '61 car, featuring a finely textured grille set beneath a wide chromed header that displayed IMPERIAL in block letters. Flanking the prominent grille were twin sets of freestanding headlamps. Each was encased in an individual chrome pod in the classic tradition, suspended from the undersides of the protruding front fenders. The whole ensemble had a crisp, tight look compared with the more rounded 1961 design. The Imperial's front fender and door treatment mimicked that of its lesser brothers, but the rear quarter featured a single horizontal blade, much shorter than the one in front, flowing back into the decklid. Perched atop each rear blade was one of the famous "gunsight" taillights, which dated back to 1955. Of all the proposed senior S-series cars, the Imperial was the handsomest, DeSoto the least attractive.

At the start of the program, the equally new S-series Plymouth and Dodge were slated to be full-size cars in the usual sense. The initial design proposals looked something like the smaller '62 production models that finally emerged. But the originals were better proportioned because of the longer wheelbase contemplated. Highlight of the line was to be a Plymouth Sport Fury two-door coupe with a roof-and-backlight treatment like the one used on the Chevrolet Camaro/Pontiac Firebird of nearly a decade later. There was to be only one window per side, confined to the door, which was cut into a heavily sculptured roof. Adjacent to the aft door edge opening was a wide, reverse-slant

Final styling for '62 DeSoto was locked up by February 1960.

Odd rear door and fender sculpturing was dubbed "the chicken wing."

Exner's original 1959 "theme" clay wore DeSoto nameplates.

Management abruptly canceled the proposed '62 Imperial.

Proposed '62 Imperial would have had an all-new, slightly smaller bodyshell.

B-pillar, and behind that an enormous wraparound rear window, V-shaped in plan view like that on the '67 Cadillac Eldorado. A watered-down version of this design ultimately appeared on the 1964-66 Barracuda, but the original S-series Fury proposal was much better looking. However, Like Chrysler's other radical 1962 prototypes, this one never reached production.

The final 1962 DeSoto styling models were ready in February of 1960. Then, the whole S-series program was pushed into the background as a brewing scandal shook Chrysler Corporation. On April 28, 1960, William C. Newberg was elected president after 27 years with the company; just two months later, on June 30, he was fired by the board of directors for alleged conflict of interest. Other officials were also dismissed, each "resignation" reported in big newspaper headlines.

During his brief tenure as president, however, Newberg was able to alter the '62 program substantially. Through his industry contacts, Newberg had heard that Chevrolet was planning to downsize its Impala. This, of course, proved false: the Impala stayed the same size, though the smaller Chevy II did arrive that season as a companion line. But Newberg was convinced it was the *Impala* that would shrink in line with the compact-car trend then sweeping the industry. As a result, he summarily ordered the Plymouth and Dodge lines downsized from a 118- to a 116-inch wheelbase. Confusion reigned as designers, modelers, and engineers worked long hours making the original S-series styling fit the shorter chassis. In the process, Exner's designs were severely compromised, losing their curved side glass together with the interesting sport coupe body style.

What ended up in the showrooms looked more like overgrown Valiants and Lancers than the sleek machines they might have been. The public was not impressed. The smaller Plymouths and Dodges went on sale in the fall of 1961, and met a poor reception. It was so poor, in fact, that Virgil Exner, too, was fired, replaced by Elwood Engel who had been lured over from Ford. This was not the first time Chrysler had tried downsizing unsuccessfully: its decision to bring out a line of compact 1953-54 models led to Chrysler's permanent loss of second place in the industry to Ford. The firm's third attempt at downsizing, the 1981 K-car compacts (Dodge Aries and Plymouth Reliant), may be more successful. At least this time they'll have plenty of company.

At first scheduled to appear along with the downsized '62 Plymouth and Dodge, the new DeSoto, Chrysler, and Imperial bodies were quickly canceled as company officials started having second thoughts in the face of an apparently changing market. Instead, the existing Chrysler and Imperial shells were noticeably facelifted for 1962. Both lost their flamboyant fins, and Chrysler gained a cheaper 300 model to trade on the prestige of the letter-series cars.

Briefly, there was supposed to be a DeSoto derivative of the facelifted '62 Chrysler Newport. An ornamentation drawing of this car was released by

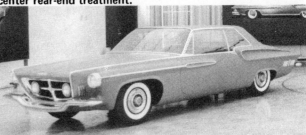

Thankfully, production '62 Plymouth was spared this off-center rear-end treatment.

An early 1959 attempt to give the Chrysler 300 a "different" look.

From the rear, 300 clay displays the "blade" bumpers Exner favored.

Engineering. It showed that the only difference between the two was the badge on the grille. Whether the company ever seriously intended to sell the car is doubtful. Indeed, it may have been created solely so that Chrysler could tell the press, which was asking pointed questions about DeSoto's future, that the company was indeed working on new models.

As for the stillborn S-series DeSoto, Fred Reynolds remembers having the chance to inspect the completed metal prototype six months after the program was killed. He recalled the car looking grotesque, awkward, and already dated. In retrospect, he was glad the corporation had decided not to build it. Given the poor showing of its Plymouth and Dodge relatives, perhaps it's just as well DeSoto died when it did. For 1963, Chrysler presented a clean-lined Valiant, Dart, and Chrysler with nary a trace of the XNR (though all the company's '63 cars were designed under Exner before he left). Long-hood/short-deck styling was forgotten until April 1964, when Ford made it really popular with a cute little car called Mustang. It wouldn't be until 1970 that Chrysler would take another fling at what became known as the "ponycar" look.

War Casualties:

1943-45 Fords,
Mercurys, and Lincolns

If World War II hadn't come along, Ford's 1943-45 models would have appeared in completely new clothes. The '43 Fords and Mercurys would have looked as little like their 1942 counterparts as the '41 Fords looked like 1940 models. Changes to Lincolns were made less often than on Fords and Mercurys, mainly because the Zephyr's bridge-truss unitized body construction and lower sales volume made major revamping relatively expensive. Since the Lincoln line had been radically facelifted for '42, the 1943 models would have been changed only in detail.

Bob Gregorie, Ford's director of styling from 1935 to 1948, recalled that the tremendous surge of work toward what would have become the 1943-45 models came to a screeching halt with the outbreak of war: "Suddenly, overnight, everything and everybody stopped. All at once the whole company changed gears and got down to war work. My styling staff started on projects like designing camouflage and engineering gliders and B-24 airframes—stuff like that. Yet, in the backs of our minds, we knew that after the war we were going to have to start building cars again. At the beginning, nobody knew whether the U.S. would win or not, but there seemed little point in planning on any assumption except that we would. So slowly, in between wartime assignments, this little skeleton group we held together would go back to the sort of nebulous business of designing after-the-war cars.

"The Ford lines were the ones we worked on most, because they were past due for a change. Edsel Ford was very busy with war production matters in 1942, but did spend what time he could with us on future planning. This lasted until his illness and death in the spring of 1943. The elder Mr. Ford took virtually no interest in design or styling activities, leaving this phase of operations to Mr. Edsel Ford and myself. There were no committees, etc., as is the usual practice. Decisions were quick and simple, which possibly accounts for some of the cleaner, simpler, straightforward styling we were able to accomplish. Mr. Edsel Ford and I were usually pretty much in agreement.

"Included later on our staff was a cross-section of men from the great coachbuilding companies. Most of the established custom body makers had folded by this time. Thus, Tom Hibbard of Hibbard & Darrin became my assistant. Martin Regitko, formerly with the Willoughby Co., headed our body draftsman group. Hermann Brunn, Charlie Waterhouse, and several others were from the old custom body companies that had formerly built coachwork for the original Lincolns. Other names I should mention include Ray Farkas, Ross Cousins, and various boys in the department. Cousins was a commercial illustrator whom we brought in to specialize in presentation renderings of the staff's design ideas.

"What was intended as the larger Ford became the first all-new postwar Mercury. I'm sure you can see the similarities between our wartime Ford clays and the production 1949-51 Mercury. At the time, we considered this design for the Ford of that era. Then, an entirely new Ford was developed, with lighter construction, new suspension, etc., and this became the 1949 Ford.

"When the tide of war began to change, we were able to put increased effort into postwar planning, but even at this point, any full-scale production from new tooling was still perhaps four years away. We had plenty of time to probe the various possibilities. This accounts for some confusion in identifying clearly many of the quarter- and full-sized models made during that time. It's hard to say whether or not there was any actual intent of producing them. Several can be considered general styling ideas.

"One idea we had back then, and it came to fruition in 1949, was to associate the Mercury more closely with the Lincoln via certain body interchanges, as well as tie them together in advertising, sales, etc. Before, the Merc was based on the Ford. We figured the Mercury might gain some prestige by becoming a baby Lincoln, rather than a blown-up Ford.

"So during the war, our Lincoln designs did have some importance toward that end. We laid down the basic lines for what would become the 1949 Mercury in a painting that Ross Cousins did in 1943. That painting showed a five-passenger coupe driving past the Rouge plant. We called it a Lincoln, but the profile is very much what the 1949 Mercury became. Then too, all those early Lincoln clays show a lot more of what we

1943 Ford would have had a more integrated grille.

Volvo-like wagon was part of Ford's small car project.

This production Ford got a trial facelift in '42.

The same treatment was applied to this prewar Mercury.

had in mind for the Mercury—as well as the Lincoln Cosmopolitan.

"As for the Continental, we weren't too sure about that one. We didn't know whether it would be continued after Mr. Edsel Ford's death in 1943. We made some

War Casualties

renderings and full-size models of the Cosmo with a spare tire mounted on the trunk, but it was too ponderous and clumsy to project the true Continental image. I think the only reason Ford Motor Company kept the Continental after the war was because they already had the body tooling. If the 1946-48 Continental hadn't used 1942 tooling, it probably wouldn't have been built those years. With the strong demand for postwar cars, the Continental did sell, and it really carried Lincoln prestige into the postwar period and to later Continentals. After Mr. Edsel Ford's death, though, no one had the heart to come up with a completely new Continental design."

We asked Mr. Gregorie about the Buicks and Chevrolets visible in the backgrounds of some of these photos. Were those cars used as inspiration? "We always had a representative group of other makes on hand," he said. "It was company policy to buy a couple of about every car made. We called them 'foreign cars,'

and we'd take them completely apart and and inspect them piece by piece—lay them out on long tables. This way, we could see all the little tricks every manufacturer used in putting his cars together—everything from seat cushion construction to new types of clips and hangers.

"We'd buy these 'foreign cars' from local dealers. Whenever I had to go anywhere on a trip, I'd always drive one of them. When we traded these cars back to the dealers, each car had been completely disassembled and then reassembled. But of course we had no specs to go by, so it was put back together the best way we knew how—and sometimes that wasn't too good. Anyway, the dealers would advertise these as 'low-mileage' used cars, which they were, but the new owners could be in real trouble due to non-production put-togethers. Nothing really fit the way it should."

The upgraded 1949 Mercury that Gregorie mentioned was not supposed to resemble the Lincoln—an important historical point. The original plan called for two separate models between Ford and the big Lincoln: the Mercury on a 116-inch wheelbase, and the

A hint of the '49 is revealed in this 1943 sketch by Ross Cousins.

Integrated fenders began evolving by April 1942. This clay would evolve into the '49 Mercury.

The first full-size Mercury clay was a "stretch" of the stillborn postwar small car (see page 47).

Moving toward the "bathtub" look, this scale model is probably a Lincoln study.

Another Lincoln model shows a grille theme like that used for 1946-48.

Opposite side of above clay has a different front fender shape.

Lincoln-Zephyr on a 118-inch chassis. The Zephyr would have had the "baby Lincoln" styling Gregorie recalls, while the '49 Mercury would have continued as a more luxurious Ford. The Ford line would have included a standard full-size model and a small car with front-wheel drive (see Chapter 12).

In the end, Ford abandoned both the postwar Zephyr and its front-drive compact (though tooling and designs for the latter ended up in France as the Ford Vedette). Mercury was moved up to the 118-inch chassis (the standard Ford rode a 114-inch wheelbase) and became, as Gregorie stated, more of a Lincoln than a Ford relation.

There was a funny thing about all these wartime machinations, and Gregorie sums it up perfectly: "It never dawned on any of us that right after the war, anything on wheels would sell, whether it was restyled or not. We just never sat down and thought about it enough to figure that out. So we went right ahead as though the first thing we'd have to do after the war was restyle the Ford and Mercury, not realizing until the last minute that a suitable facelift would do as well. In fact,

we had until about 1948-49 before we'd have to come up with anything really different."

It is interesting to compare these wartime Ford designs to what Chrysler was doing at the same time (Chapter 5) because of their considerable similarity. Not that Ford and Chrysler were sharing ideas, or that any "corporate espionage" was going on. Both companies were merely moving with the general trends of the era: rounded, integrated fenders, broad glass areas, skirted wheel wells, ornament-free hoods, wraparound bumpers, and "all-of-a-piece" grilles. Crisper shapes didn't emerge at Chrysler until 1949, or at Ford until 1952. It does seem, though, that the wartime Chrysler products would have had a definite styling edge on the mid-'40s Fords, Lincolns, and Mercurys had the war not interrupted things. Chrysler's glass wrapped more, its window frames were thinner, its grilles were better integrated, and the overall lines of its cars were more smooth-flowing.

The war did intervene, of course, and the sales figures tell what happened in later years. And don't forget, GM had something to do with it, too.

Vertical grille theme on this Lincoln clay was years ahead of Edsel.

This proposed facelift for '46 grafted on to a '42 Lincoln wasn't used.

Postwar Mercury became a "baby Lincoln." This was the design thinking in May 1942.

Ford products wouldn't be this streamlined until the '50s.

Lincoln mock-up from 1943 shows heavy Buick and Olds influences.

'49 Lincoln was based directly on this wartime study. Hidden headlamps didn't make production.

Ford's First Postwar Compact:

Too Little Too Soon

Thoughts of a small postwar Ford started a flurry of design and model-making activity in Dearborn as early as 1942. The first ideas centered on a low-priced four-cylinder model using the dimensions, power output, weight, and price of the pre-war Willys-Overland as targets. Later, it appears some Ford executives saw its new car as a rival for the Studebaker Champion in size and price. The Champion, of course, had a six-cylinder engine, and its dimensions had grown from 1939 to 1942. It turned out that Studebaker based its entire postwar line on the Champion, with dramatic restyling planned for 1947.

As a result, Ford's small-car studies in 1943-44 were aimed at a moving target. But there was no panic, no mad rush to "catch up" with the competition. The company had always prepared its advance projects against hypothetical new models—just in case. These programs were a necessary but stimulating activity—especially for the lucky few associated with them.

Advance planning was strangely disorganized in those days. Initiatives were taken by various departments independently of one another and without central coordination—a reflection of the chaotic command situation in 1943. Chief engineer Lawrence Sheldrich had left that year, and a replacement wasn't found for some time. Also, Edsel Ford, president of the company, died in 1943, his 81-year-old father resuming the functions of chief executive officer despite his drift into senility. With all this, Edsel's son, Henry Ford II, was hurriedly brought home from the service. His education as future president and chairman began with his appointment as executive vice-president. As such, he was informed of everything that was going on, and took part in discussions of all plans for the future.

In late spring 1944, a group of executives led by sales manager John R. Davis and production boss Mead L. Bricker came to young Henry with the idea for forming a separate committee to prepare new products for the postwar market. This became the Engineering Planning Committee, representing key departments from manufacturing to market research. Hudson McCarroll took the lead in defining future products and their technical makeup. This included what he saw as a new kind of economy car, designed to sell at two-thirds the price of the standard-size Ford.

The committee looked at the company's last small-car project from before the war. This was known by

code number 92-A, and was completed in 1938 by a team led by Eugene Farkas, who had played a big part in designing the Model A, Model B, and the Ford V-8. Project 92-A was quite small, about 600 pounds lighter than the standard-size Ford, with a shorter wheelbase and a narrower track. Cleverly, Farkas had proposed using the anemic V-8/60 for this car rather than developing and tooling up for a new four- or six-cylinder engine. But Project 92-A was scrapped because of high production costs. As calculated in 1938, they would have been too close to those of the big cars to give the smaller model a significant price advantage. Ford planners knew the cost/profit problem would be even more troublesome in the postwar world.

Ford had produced various smaller cars in Europe before the war, starting in 1932 with the four-cylinder British Model Y Junior, a Sheldrick design. Ford of Germany began building the four-cylinder Eifel in 1935, switching to the Taunus in 1939. All these were considered too small for American buyers, however, and they offered nothing technically that could be profitably applied to a smaller U.S. model. The British-made Ford Royal, the German Ford V-8, and the French Matford were all powered by the same 2.2-liter 60-bhp V-8 engine. They were the right size, but even less up-to-date than the four-cylinder European models, especially in suspension, brakes, driveline, and body design. Using them as a basis for a new American model after 1945 was out of the question (although the Royal did return in England with a facelifted body as the Ford Pilot in 1948).

Clearly, the new small American Ford had to be

designed from scratch in Dearborn. Because there were no existing components suitable for it, engineers were free to toy with entirely new concepts.

Frantic and furious work brought forth many ideas—some intelligent, some much less so. One featured front-wheel drive and a four-cylinder engine installed transversely ahead of the front wheel axis. The radiator was placed slightly higher than the engine and behind it, backed by a cowl structure that carried the fuel tank. This made for a short hood and a low flat floor for unusually generous interior space. Another had a conventional chassis with an inline five-cylinder engine. This was the elder Henry's doing. Although he was ostensibly no longer connected with the com-

pany's product engineering, he still maintained a private laboratory where he had been toying with five-cylinder engines since about 1936.

Soon, the engine experimental department was humming with new and original powerplant designs. Air-cooled four- and six-cylinder engines were built and tested. Cast-aluminum cylinder blocks were tried for several water-cooled units, including the five-cylinder job, but were ruled out as too costly. Rear-mounted engines were not even considered. Front-wheel drive was quickly discarded because of its many unknowns in addition to its high costs.

As time went on, the small V-8 was increasingly preferred, along with other basic design elements of Farkas' 1938 proposal. A new prototype incorporating its main features was completed in mid-1944. In September, Henry Ford II announced his company intended to produce a smaller, lower-priced model.

Eugene T. "Bob" Gregorie, director of Ford Styling, had been doing sketches and clay models of small cars for two years when the Engineering Planning Committee ordered full-scale versions that winter. A 98-inch wheelbase was selected, and a fastback two-door sedan was the first body style developed. The overall proportions that emerged were quite similar to the standard-size '42 Ford's, but the lines were more modern, with a slab-sided body and a lower, wider grille. A continuing flow of fresh market information led to completion of several prototypes that differed in many ways from each other. These were further modified and a 100-inch wheelbase was tried. Although the five-cylinder engine was still in the running at this point, development was concentrated around the V-8/60.

In January 1945, the small car was defined more precisely than before, and planners settled on the 100-inch wheelbase. Within six months, the five-cylinder engine had been scrapped, and development work went ahead on the V-8 alone. The frame was designed as a smaller version of the Ford and Mercury

This coupe version was also tried. By now, planners had settled on a 100-inch wheelbase. Styling similarity to '49 Mercury is strong.

Ford's First Compact

chassis being prepared for 1949. Replacing the old transverse leaf springs front and rear were a coil-spring independent front suspension and parallel rear leaf springs. This suspension was adapted for the small car as well.

Clyde R. Paton, former chief engineer of Packard, was hired to direct the project from prototype to production-ready stage. His understanding was that the car should start coming off the lines within six months after the end of the war in Europe. But the small car soon ran into the same snag that killed Farkas' project: cost.

Because it was designed as a scaled-down big car, the small car had approximately the same number of parts, so assembly operations and labor costs were similar. Material savings were relatively minor, as there was little to take out of the body structure and sheetmetal to reduce costs. Use of a standard production engine was already planned, along with gearboxes and axles derived from, or closely akin to, those already being built—no savings there. Cutting back on trim and equipment wouldn't lead to any significant savings, either—only to dull, drab cars that dealers would have nothing to do with. As a result, the project was put on the back burner. It might have died completely had it not been for Maurice Dollfus, a prominent Paris banker and president of Ford France.

Had the Light Car been produced, its interior would have been sparsely trimmed to hold down price.

Ford planned a full range of body styles for its postwar compact. These early drawings used the 98-inch wheelbase.

The French factory was getting ready to turn out a slightly rejuvenated Matford to get production going again. Dollfus came to Dearborn in the summer of 1945 and saw the small-car prototypes then on test. Originally, he had planned to concentrate future production on a four-cylinder model based on the German Taunus. Dollfus was enthusiastic about the 100-inch-wheelbase American design, imprudently forgetting the realities of the postwar European market. For most buyers, the only sensible alternative to a four-cylinder model was a twin (Dyna Panhard, Citroen 2CV). Few could afford to buy and maintain a six, much less an eight. But Ford was equipped to build the V-8/60 in France and Dollfus liked the new car designed around that engine. Now, if only his Dearborn bosses would let him have it . . .

Within Ford, there was still a lot of support for the Light Car, but its fate seemed to hinge on cost. Before it was replaced by a new Products Committee holding greater decision-making power, the ad-hoc Engineering Planning Committee had been rebuffed by a report that the Light Car's production cost would come within 17 percent of the standard-size models'. This was an insufficient margin for going ahead with production.

Hudson McCarroll, who had been officially promoted to engineering director in 1945, didn't know how to handle this hot potato—and ended up listening to everybody. Sales manager Davis had a buyer for every car Ford could build. Why put a lot of money into a brand-new model that the public might not accept? He saw no need for a smaller car—even as a loss leader—until 1948 or '49 at the earliest. In that event, Clyde Paton thought it would be necessary to redesign the car completely—preferably with a unit body. As a result, the 100-inch-wheelbase prototype was shelved.

Ford built several Light Car prototypes. This is one of the later ones, shown at Dearborn in early 1945. By this time, only the two-door sedan was planned for production.

A new, somewhat larger car was ordered for a possible 1948-49 introduction. The four-cylinder economy-car project was handed over to the research department. At this stage, an air-cooled rear engine was considered for the first time, but probably not seriously.

Paton and his staff went to work on two larger versions of the Light Car, one with a 106-inch wheelbase to be sold as a Ford, the other with a 112-inch wheelbase for the Mercury nameplate. To handle development and production, Ford created a new Light Car Division in April 1946. By then, the program was seen as so important that no one questioned a corporate reorganization of this scale. But the raw materials supply situation soon burst Ford's small-car bubble.

In the immediate postwar years, steel, copper, lead, zinc, and other metals were hard to come by. Henry Ford II knew it was not good business to add a whole new model line to vie for scarce resources with cars that were already selling well. Although management did not officially stop small-car development, the Product Committee told the Light Car Division to defer production plans in 1946. The result was the same: the Light Car was dead in Ford's U.S. future. But by then, the 106-inch-wheelbase version was fully engineered and could be considered a production prototype.

The Light Car's production problems in the U.S. made it easier for Dollfus to argue in favor of building it in France. In June 1946, Dearborn's engineering department released all data and blueprints to him. The decision not to build the Light Car in America may have already been made by then, though it wasn't formally announced until September.

The engineering staff at Poissy redesigned the 106-inch-wheelbase prototype for production on metric tools, and adjusted specifications to suit local suppliers

of electrical equipment, instrumentation, radiators, and the like. Under the name Vedette, it started coming from the French factory in the fall of 1948. The name Vedette has a double meaning: a small, speedy boat used by the French Navy, and a general term for a star in the entertainment universe. Making its bow at the *Salon de l'Automobile* in Paris that October, the Vedette was overshadowed by Peugeot's new 203—and both were eclipsed by the Citroen 2CV (Renault's 4CV and the Dyna Panhard had debuted the previous year).

With its high fuel consumption, not even a reasonable price could make the Vedette a success. Few Frenchmen bought them, and export sales proved elusive. So, the Vedette has the somewhat dubious distinction of being both a "never-was" in the U.S. and an "also-ran" overseas.

The Light Car was sent to Ford's French subsidiary and became the 1948 Vedette. It didn't sell very well.

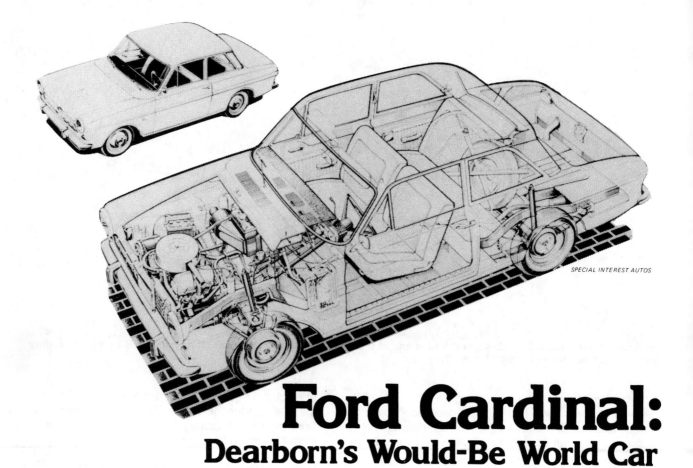

Ford Cardinal:
Dearborn's Would-Be World Car

The Cardinal grew out of Ford's plan for a "world car." The idea was to come up with a design that could be marketed in various countries and would also be suitable for local production. The car would be designed to accommodate mechanical components from multiple sources, primarily Ford's own factories around the world.

Early in world-car planning, it was suggested the United States be included in both production and marketing. This stemmed from the fact that, by 1956, imports were taking a growing chunk of U.S. car sales. Volkswagen's Beetle was already popular, and backed by a solid sales and service organization. Renault was beginning to make inroads with its Dauphine. Both of these rear-engine models were designed for low manufacturing costs and high production volume. They were exported in vast numbers, and also assembled locally in some countries. They were "world cars" in a way, though they were aimed mainly at European buyers.

Despite these successes, imports didn't worry Ford in the mid-'50s. The small-car market wasn't large enough yet to justify the expense of developing an import-fighter. Ford would have had to sell at least 250,000 a year just to break even, and the nation just wasn't buying that many small cars. Besides, Volkswagen had carved out its niche in the market, and could be expected to fight hard to keep it. So, a U.S.-only economy model made little sense. But with a

world-car scheme, Ford could accomplish three things: take a share of small-car sales away from foreign producers, develop Ford's own small-car technology, and provide a more accurate reading of consumer preferences.

Still, there was no great hurry on this. At the time, Ford was preoccupied with expanding its product line—mainly upwards—in size and price. The sporty Thunderbird was in production, the prestigious Mark II had been launched, and Ford's Louisville plant was being tooled up for the much-ballyhooed Edsel. But there *were* signs of change. The success of American Motors and its compact Rambler had taken the Big Three by surprise. Despite the failure of the Aero-Willys, Hudson Jet, and Henry J, the market for compacts was expanding, and Rambler dealers were cashing in. So, while one group of Ford marketeers and product planners considered the "world car," another began toying with compact-car concepts.

Eventually, it was suggested the two groups get together on a new product for domestic production only. This led management to order four small-car designs worked up in full detail. Two of these paper cars were done in Europe, one by the British engineering staff at Dagenham, one at Ford-Werke in Cologne, Germany. The other two originated in Dearborn, and were, inevitably, bigger and heavier than the European proposals.

From England came a conventional front-engine/

rear-drive design, sized between the British Ford Prefect and Consul then being built. The German offering was much more original, with front-wheel drive and a lot of engineering ideas taken from the Goliath, a small front-drive car made by Borgward in Bremen. That was hardly surprising since August Momberger, who had been lured to Cologne about 1954, had been one of Borgward's top engineers.

Late in 1957, Dearborn planners sat down to study the four proposals. Uppermost in the mind of President Ernest R. Breech were rumors that GM and Chrysler were working on compacts—rumors backed by solid evidence from Ford's "spies." The import threat seemed puny against the prospect of new mass-produced Chevrolet and Plymouth small cars, sold through powerful dealer networks. Consequently, Breech approved one of the Dearborn designs—a six-cylinder, six-passenger car that eventually became the 1960 Falcon.

Ford's engineering office under Earle S. Mac-Pherson gave the Falcon top priority, and the manufacturing staff got it into production late in 1959. People in Dearborn had apparently forgotten the "world car." But not everyone. A few engineers worried that Breech had made the wrong move, and decided to take a fresh approach. Their idea was to develop a car that would compete directly with the Volkswagen, but not as a "Super" Volkswagen. Just as tanks are stopped by tank-destroyers, the Beetle's march in the U.S. would be stopped by an "anti-Beetle."

Noise, lack of space, and poor directional stability were seen as the German car's weak points. To beat VW on space, Dearborn's baby would have to be bigger. It would have to be boxier, too, because of the requirement that wheelbase be 100 inches or less. To beat the VW in quietness, Ford would need a water-cooled engine (and had several suitable units already available in Europe). To beat the VW on stability, the engine would have to be mounted in front. So far, both the British and German paper cars would qualify as a basis for the "anti-Beetle." But one of the VW's strong selling points was its good traction: it could climb slippery hills and crawl out of mud or snow because its driving wheels carried most of the weight. Since Ford wanted a front engine for stability, its new car would need front-wheel drive for best traction.

The drawings from Ford-Werke were taken off the shelf. A fleet of small front-wheel-drive cars, mainly Goliaths and Saabs, were brought to Dearborn for evaluation (later, they would be used as test rigs for experimental components). As the design took shape, British Ford engineer Roy Lunn vetoed the use of a transfer chain to take the power flow from the crankshaft to the transaxle. He considered it too costly and too noisy, with important friction losses and questionable reliability. But no other obvious driveline existed to mate with the inline four-cylinder engine chosen for Project A, as it was now known.

The little Goliath hinted at a solution. Borgward's economy car used a flat-four engine positioned ahead of the front wheel axis, with the transmission placed

Cardinal prototype poses with contemporary Rambler American in this 1961 photo.

Cardinal resembled the Rambler from the rear, too, except for teardrop taillights.

behind the final drive/differential. The horizontally opposed cylinders (two per bank) made the engine so short that it fit easily within a normal front overhang space. Ford didn't want to copy the Goliath engine: it was too close to the VW design, and the company had no recent experience with flat-four engines. But Ford did have a solid background in V-type configurations. A short, small-displacement V-4 would solve the driveline and space problems just as well.

It was determined that a narrow-angle V-4 (20 degrees between cylinder banks) allowed for the simplest block casting and the least weight. Also, it needed only one cylinder head, which would help keep manufacturing costs down. But the cylinders had to be staggered, and it was difficult to find room for adequate-size bearings. The connecting rods could be properly mounted only by going to a two-main-bearing crankshaft, but that led to roughness, noise, and vibration problems that a separate balance shaft could not eliminate.

The next step was to try a 60-degree V-4, where connecting rods from opposite cylinders could share crankpins. This layout required two cylinder heads and was heavier, but gave acceptable noise levels. Because it retained a balance shaft—a counterweighted shaft turning in the opposite direction from the crankshaft—engineers were able to control inherent vibration characteristics quite well. The first test engine had 1100cc (67 cubic-inch) displacement, and was installed in a Saab early in 1959. Swift development of the powertrain followed in the spring.

Meanwhile, Ford Styling was brought in to shape the package. To provide seating dimensions comparable to those of other Ford products, the initial 91-inch

Ford Cardinal:

wheelbase was stretched, first to 94 inches, and later to 97.5 inches. This also made for better-balanced exterior proportions.

Chassis engineers were also hard at work. Roy Lunn had proposed attaching the front suspension to the engine/transmission assembly, rather than the unit-construction body. The idea was to keep road shock and other disturbances from reaching the body structure. But this meant that the car would, in a sense, be pulled along by its engine mounts, a somewhat less-than-ideal arrangement. Ford went ahead and tried it, and it apparently worked well enough to get the go-ahead for further development. At first, the suspension linkage consisted of upper and lower A-arms, with short torsion bars. This was redesigned and simplified, though it ended up considerably heavier. To provide lateral location, the upper control arms gave way to a transverse leaf spring, which also made the torsion bars unnecessary. The rear suspension was cart-like in its simplicity, a scaled-down copy of the front suspension from Ford's pickups, using an I-beam axle on semi-elliptic leaf springs.

The first Project A prototype was submitted to Ford's product-planning committee in June 1959. By that time, foreign cars were taking 10 percent of the market, Renault was closing fast on Volkswagen's lead, BMC was beginning to import the front-drive Mini, and England's Rootes Group was offering its new Hillman Minx. Ford had earlier brought in a small number of its British Anglias and Prefects in response to GM selling of German Opels through Buick outlets and Vauxhalls through Pontiac dealers. Though not sold here in large numbers, Ford's "captive" imports showed that the company was beginning to take foreign-car sales seriously—and that management was undecided about how to tackle the market.

Robert S. McNamara, then vice-president in charge of the car and truck group, approved funds for further development of Project A, which began to acquire various code names—Oriole, Hummingbird, Falcon Four—and was becoming a serious contender for domestic production. More Saabs were purchased and fitted with Ford V-4 engines, while the Styling section restyled the short, boxy, two-door notchback sedan to give it a family resemblance with the Falcon.

By January 1960, even Henry Ford II was beginning to take an interest. Up to this time, the program had no definite timetable, and engineers worked on it with only the vague idea that they were supposed to have a production-ready prototype finished in time for the 1965 model year. Because the Falcon had quickly become the country's best-selling compact, Ford's fortunes were riding high. That success made HF II eager to take on the imports for what he hoped would be a stunning one-two sales punch. As a result, he ordered a crash program to get the Cardinal—the project's latest code-name—into production as a 1963

model. That decision would have big implications for Ford-Werke in Germany as well.

The Cardinal was far from finished in 1960, though it was being designed with an eye to production. But getting factories ready for such a radically different car posed tremendous problems for Dearborn—especially under HF II's close deadline. The biggest problem was that the Cardinal had many special parts, such as constant-velocity universal joints, shared with no other current Ford product. These would have to be ordered from outside suppliers who would need time to tool up for volume production.

The Germans faced a different problem. Ford-Werke had designed and developed a new Taunus to replace its old 12-M, which had become dated in both looks and road manners. With its rear drive and advanced overhead-cam inline four-cylinder engine, the new model was intended to win European buyers away from Opel, Renault, Fiat, and Volkswagen, and looked entirely up to the task. But the new Taunus first had to be approved by Dearborn, where product planners noticed a similarity in package size and overall purpose between this car and the American Cardinal. Ford's bean-counters figured the company could make big savings in development costs by producing the Cardinal in both the U.S. and Germany. That was the end of the German-designed Taunus, which never got beyond the prototype stage. Ford-Werke directors were told that "their" new model was being designed in America, and that specifications, blueprints, and a list of tooling requirements would follow in due course.

The design that Henry Ford II had tentatively okayed in June 1960 was for a two-door sedan built on a 99.5-inch wheelbase, with an overall length of 167 inches and a height of 54.5 inches. The target curb weight of 1700 pounds would prove impossible to meet. The suggested retail price was set at $1650—a cut-rate figure that meant bare-bones interior trim and little convenience equipment. The price also dictated skimping on such vital items as tires, and only the cheapest two-ply 13-inchers were specified for the Cardinal.

The American model was supposed to have a top speed of 80 mph, so it was necessary to enlarge the engine to 1500cc (91 cubic inches) for an output of 75 bhp at 4700 rpm on a compression ratio of 8.5:1 (for regular-grade gasoline). For the European version, Ford was satisfied with a 70-mph top speed, which meant reducing its engine size to 1200cc (73 cubic inches) for 52 bhp at 4200 rpm on a 7.15:1 compression ratio. Engines and gearboxes for both Cardinals were to be made in Germany, while sheetmetal stampings and certain chassis components would be made in America. It was calculated that the economies of scale obtained by sourcing the most expensive components this way would leave a handsome profit on each car—even after the costs of two-way transatlantic shipping were figured in.

The German version was to be assembled at the Cologne plant, while the U.S. model would be built at Louisville, now that the Edsel was no more. A

Here is [...] would have been marketed as the Redwing V-4. *ELIMINATE X*

right-ha[...]
the loca[...]
was hig[...]
weight in[...]
which ha[...]
at Dager[...]
designs [...]
named A[...]
dinal. Th[...]
which wa[...]

Ford's [...]
came in [...]
scheduled[...]
company [...]
other fact[...]
other word[...]
the financ[...]

name, but by spring, Ford's publicity men were working on advertisements for the "Redwing." (The Cardinal name would be thought to have undesirable connotations, especially among Catholics.)

But that's as far as it got. The Cardinal/Redwing was suddenly canceled in May, after Ford Division general manager Lee A. Iacocca and company president John Dykstra learned the car's true production costs. The Redwing would have been more expensive to build than the Falcon—and since it was smaller, it would have had to sell at a lower price.

The upshot was that Ford-Werke was stuck with an American-designed front-drive car it never wanted (despite the Rhinebank roots in Momberger's 1956 proposal). But in September 1962, production of the Taunus 12-M began. And through various successor models, it lived on through 1970.

The VW Beetle meets Ford's "anti-Beetle." Front fender emblem marks this as the production German Taunus 12-M.

Near Misses:

Ford's Post-1957 Two-Seaters

Did Ford abandon thoughts of a two-seat sports car after the '57 Thunderbird? Not by a long shot. Between 1957 and the mid-'60s, enthusiastic designers nurtured dreams of a car to fill the void left when the two-seat T-Bird's four-seat replacement appeared for 1958. Some of those dreams evolved rather far before the company wrote them off.

The decision to build the larger, coil-sprung, semi-unit-body '58 "Squarebird" is impossible to fault. Though Ford had sold some 50,000 of the 1955-57 two-seat models, the biggest factor limiting the T-Bird's market acceptance had been its passenger capacity. Creating a four-seater with the luxury and individuality of the original two-seat Thunderbird was the obvious way to go—and Ford's Robert S. McNamara was nothing if not logical. The four-seater sold up to 90,000 units annually in its best years, and Thunderbird was one of the few nameplates to score improved sales in 1958 over '57.

Because of the auto industry's three-year production lead times, Ford's decision to go to four seats was actually made in 1955—shortly after the first two-seat

T-Bird hit the streets. Through early 1956, however, it wasn't known whether the four-seater would be an addition to the line or a complete replacement for the two-seat model. As a result, Ford designers developed a two-seat Thunderbird for '58 with some of the same appearance features as the four-seater that took shape alongside it.

Since the 1957 'Bird had a fairly comprehensive facelift, plans for '58 called for only minor styling changes. The two-seater would have acquired the quad taillights and headlights that appeared on the larger 'Bird, along with its sculptured bodyside "bombs" and combination bumper/grille. Eventually, however, McNamara put a firm "stop" on the 1958 two-seater project. Said Tom Case, then Thunderbird product planning manager, "I think he felt that nothing should take away from the impact of the four-seater, and that was where our profits lay—which, of course, was correct."

In 1960 Ford Division took on a new and enthusiastic general manager named Lee Iacocca, who instituted a sprucing-up of all its various model lines. Iacocca first suggested a youth-oriented sporty car with the flavor of the original two-seat T-Bird in 1961, and an informal eight-man committee was set up to explore the possibilities. The group determined that a sizable and growing market did want such a car, but whether it should have room for just two passengers or more than that wasn't clear. As we now know, Ford again decided in favor of four seats; the Mustang appeared in the spring of 1964—and was an instant success. But along the way, memories of the original T-Bird inspired many proposals for two-seat sports or sporting cars. Two of these were the Mustang I and the XT-Bird.

Mustang I was designed by stylist Gene Bordinat, engineer Herb Misch, and product planner Roy Lunn. It was first displayed publicly at the U.S. Grand Prix at Watkins Glen in October 1962. Conceived as Ford's answer to the Triumph TR3 and the MGA, this 90-inch-wheelbase sportster had four-wheel independent suspension and a 60-degree V-4 of 1927cc (118 cubic inches) developed from the Cardinal project (see Chapter 13). The engine was placed behind the cockpit ahead of the rear wheels, and breathed through a single-choke Solex carburetor to produce 90 bhp at 6500 rpm. A competition version with twin dual-throat Webers and a special manifold offered around 110 bhp. Bolted to the V-4 was a four-speed transaxle, also derived from the Cardinal, with a cable-operated shift linkage. A 7.5-inch-diameter clutch was adopted from the English Ford Consul. In line with British sports cars of the day, Mustang I used disc brakes at the front and drums at the rear, with a parking brake operating on the rear drums. The discs were English Girlings, and the 13-inch mag wheels were built to Ford's spec by Lotus.

Because it weighed a mere 1200 pounds, the Mustang I was a lively performer, capable of 115 mph and excellent fuel economy. The swoopy styling was very well conceived, although Bordinat had seen it through in just 21 days. The prototype was seen with a cut-down racing windscreen, which would have been replaced in production by a full windshield. There was no provision for a soft top on this open car, though a lightweight folding hardtop was developed. Both these items wouldn't have added more than a couple hundred pounds to the curb weight. With its racing windshield, the Mustang I stood only 40 inches high, though its ground clearance was nearly five inches.

Interior styling was just as nicely executed, with a five-pod instrument panel housing fuel gauge, speedometer, tach, ammeter, and water temperature gauges. Most driver controls were mounted to the left in an angled extension of the armrest, and a passenger grab handle hung from the dashboard to the right. The nicely bucketed seats were not adjustable, but the pedals were. Most drivers found they could fit very well despite the diminutive outer dimensions.

At Watkins Glen, the Mustang I was driven in a parade lap by Dan Gurney, and the enthusiast crowd loved it. In a subsequent road test, *Car and Driver* magazine found that 0-60 mph acceleration took just 10 seconds, and fuel economy was as high as 30 mpg.

'57 T-Bird would have had this rear end for '58.

A two-seat Bird evolved alongside the '58 four-seater.

Mid-engine Mustang I was an outgrowth of the Cardinal program.

Enthusiasts loved the Mustang I, but it was too far out for Lee Iacocca.

The report compared it to a Cooper racing car, and praised everything about the Mustang I except its lack of luggage space.

But ironically, it was the enthusiasm of sports-car types that banished this mid-engine mover to never-never land. Iacocca welcomed the praise, but noted: "When I looked at the guys saying it—the offbeat

Near Misses

crowd, the real buffs—I said 'That's sure not the car we want to build, because it can't be a volume car. It's too far out.' "

Similar drawbacks plagued another early-'60s proposal, the Falcon-based XT-Bird. This idea was put forth in 1961 by Budd, a long-time Ford body supplier. Budd had tooled the original two-seat Thunderbird bodies, and still had the '57 dies. The plan was to use this tooling for a new production car based on the chassis and drivetrain of the 1961 Falcon, topped by a modified version of the '57 T-Bird shell.

The XT-Bird started as a bare Falcon chassis, but retained much of that car's underbody structure. The '57 T-Bird body was updated in appearance by shearing off its tailfins and lowering its front fenders, though ingeniously Budd managed to retain the original dashboard and cowl. In line with then-current fashion, the '57's wraparound windsheild was eliminated by substituting a less angled A-pillar with front quarter vents. As on the original T-Bird, there was a folding soft top that disappeared into a well just ahead of the decklid. Unlike the original, though, the XT-Bird had a small rear jump seat that could hold children or be dropped down to form a luggage platform. The prototype body was made of steel. Budd estimated that a production version of the XT-Bird could make a profit at a retail price of $2800.

Budd executives prepared an elaborate proposal for

The Mustang project was code-named "Allegro." This is one of many mock-ups.

Unlike the Allegro X-car (pg. 54), this model was never publicly shown.

Look closely— it's a two-seat Mustang photographed in June 1964.

Two-seat Mustang may have been intended for '65. It would have been interesting.

Ford because they knew Iacocca was looking for a sporting design. Their presentation noted the (even then) very high resale value of 1955-57 Thunderbirds, and claimed this indicated strong, unmet buyer demand for a Detroit-built sports car cheaper than the Corvette. "The total tool, jig, and fixture costs for production of the XT-Bird would not exceed $1.5 million," Budd wrote. "We could ship the entire body-in-white for the XT-Bird to the Ford Motor Company for a total unit cost of between $350 and $400 ... We believe that we could be shipping complete bodies-in-white for this car six months from the day you authorize us to start the job."

In the end, however, the XT-Bird joined the Mustang I on history's "no-go" list. Lack of full four-passenger capacity was its main drawback, as it was for the Mustang I. Additionally, it had rather dumpy lines that didn't set many hearts pounding. Ford's own styling studios would have inevitably improved it, so this probably wasn't the deciding factor. But it didn't help the presentation.

Even after the Mustang I and XT-Bird had been rejected, Ford kept playing with two-seaters, including two open models, the Median and the Mina. The Median was really a racing car, created for inspiration rather than production. The Mina was a sports-car derivation, but didn't develop beyond a single mock-up.

Next, Iacocca's planners reviewed a proposal called the "median sports car," with styling that captured much of the original Thunderbird's flavor. This was mocked up as a two-seater, a two-plus-two with jump seats, and a two-plus-two with a set of cramped rear buckets.

The median sports car led to another set of styling studies all called Aventura. There were 12 different clay models, one of which emerged as the Allegro X-car. This formed the basis for a series of cars—13 in all, each slightly different in dimensions and interior packaging. The Allegro was shown to the public in August 1963. But Ford admitted it was just wishful thinking by labeling it a "styling experimental" exercise.

The handsome Allegro was built on a 99-inch wheelbase, stood 50 inches high, and was 63.5 inches wide. Its power unit was a 144 cubic-inch overhead-valve Falcon six. The drivetrain layout was conventional: front-mounted engine with manual transmission behind, connected by a driveshaft to a live rear axle. Ford was now leaning towards off-the-shelf American drivetrain components, although designers stated the Allegro could also accommodate the 1200cc or 1500cc V-4s from the German Ford Taunus, and with that car's front-wheel-drive mechanicals. Had the V-4/front-drive arrangement been used, noted *Road & Track* magazine, "it would seem that there [would be] space for four passengers without major body alterations, and the width of the door [for rear seat entrance] bears this out."

Like the Mustang I, the Allegro's seats were fixed, but the pedals were movable to fit different-size drivers. The steering wheel was adjustable for tilt (up and down), and also swung laterally to the right, out of the way, as on contemporary production Thunderbirds. A "memory button" allowed the wheel to be returned to a preset position once the driver was seated in the cockpit. The Allegro featured retractable seat belts—certainly a portent of the future. Because the seats were fixed structural body members, the seatbelt housings were attached directly to them—a touch that showed the influence of aircraft design practice.

The Allegro and its many variations occupied the attention of Ford management for about a year, until mid-summer 1962. By that time, the theme had been worked over so much it had become stale. So, in August 1962, Bordinat, Iacocca, Donald Frey, and Henry Ford II decided to start over with a new series of clays. And this package—base price $2500, curb

Another 1964 exercise was this intriguing commuter car wearing "Colt V-4" badges.

weight 2500 pounds, length 180 inches, four seats, floorshift, Falcon mechanical components—emerged 18 months later as the Mustang. Ford kept displaying the Allegro during most of 1963, possibly as a smoke screen to hide the forthcoming Mustang. But two-seaters were never seriously considered after mid-1962.

Interestingly, however, Ford did go as far as devising a two-seat version of the production Mustang convertible. This car, possibly a fiberglass mock-up, was painted white, and had the same styling as the 1964½ four-seat model, though wheelbase was correspondingly shorter, perhaps up to 10 inches less. It was photographed in the courtyard of Ford's Styling Center on June 11, 1964, two months after the four-seater went on sale. This may indicate that a two-seat ragtop was planned for the '65 model year and dropped at the last minute. The full story may never be known.

In the early '70s, two-seat styling studies briefly surfaced again during development of what would become the Mustang II. But no one seriously doubted that that car would be anything but a four-seater. It was, and sold as well as the original Mustang 10 years earlier. Ford fans who wanted a two-place sports car thus had little choice but to spend a lot of money and buy a Pantera.

Mach 2 was an early '70s mid-engine experiment based on a shortened Mustang chassis. It wasn't seriously considered.

Gaylord:
A Dream and a Dilemma

Just after World War II a few millionaire playboys, who wanted to get in the sports-car boom started by MG and Jaguar, put their ample resources behind their very own dream cars. The majority of these turned out to be pretty ridiculous. They well attest to the remark made by the former publisher of *Road & Track* magazine, John R. Bond, that a little knowledge about cars can be right dangerous.

The brothers Gaylord were different—rich to be sure, but devoted enthusiasts and serious about their cars. Their father, who had invented the bobby pin, had been smart enough to patent that idea, assuring the family fortune. The elder Gaylord had owned Marmons, Lincolns, Packards, and Pierce-Arrows. The boys spent their youth hot-rodding Packards, Cadillacs, and LaSalles. Speed engineer Andy Granatelli once built Ed Gaylord a Packard that was the fastest thing on wheels in downtown Chicago just after World War II. The police have the records to prove it. GM's Ed Cole was a personal friend of the brothers, who spent many hours at the proving grounds examining that company's latest experimental machines.

In 1949 Jim Gaylord, the more visionary of the brothers, met with Alex Tremulis, then chief of styling at Tucker in Chicago. Tremulis recalled that Gaylord just stopped by to talk cars—but the conversation lasted

long into the night. Five years later Tremulis was at Ford, and Gaylord was visiting him again. "Alex, I'm going to build the world's finest sports car, and you're going to style it for me," Jim told his friend.

Tremulis had to refuse the assignment because he thought his employers would take a dim view of freelancing. So, he recommended Milwaukee designer Brooks Stevens instead, and Gaylord duly phoned Wisconsin. Stevens, who would later launch the Excalibur, had a great deal of experience with such firms as Alfa Romeo, Kaiser-Frazer, Willys-Overland, and American Motors. He immediately agreed to take on the project.

Gaylord's styling concept was a modern envelope body with classic overtones: namely, an upright radiator and big headlights. He wanted a 100-inch wheelbase and a retractable hardtop, too. Stevens suggested the prototype be built by Spohn of Ravensburg, West Germany. The car was set to be shown at the 1955 Paris Auto Salon.

The prototype was hastily completed and arrived just in time. It was a garish, finned affair with forward-jutting fenders. Most interesting were its freestanding front wheels—the entire wheel/tire was exposed by the cut-back fender. A two-tone panel swept rearward and upward from the fender's concave portion to form the bottom and trailing edges of the door. Stevens called this effect the "Washington Coach Door." The body colors were black and ivory, Stevens' favorites.

A more conservative second car emerged from this exercise with smaller headlights and a cleaner overall appearance, but without the interesting exposed wheels. Its retractable top was especially ingenious. The roof itself contained a recessed rear window and air vents. At the push of a button, the rear deck lifted, and a chain drive pulled the top back into the trunk. The Gaylord thus preceded the production Ford Skyliner of 1957-59 (which was considerably more complicated) by about a full year.

Jim Gaylord designed a strong chrome-moly tubular chassis, with coil springs and A-arms up front and a beam axle at the rear. The suspension was well-damped and almost impervious to shock. The engine in the first prototype was a 331-cid Chrysler hemi. Two later cars (both of which had normal wheelwells) and a body-less chassis were fitted with Cadillac V-8s. The transmission selected was Hydra-Matic, modified so that upshifts occurred only at peak revs unless the driver changed gears manually.

Loaded with standard amenities, the Gaylord was announced at a price of $14,500. That was soon revised up to $17,500, but included everything. Among the car's more unusual features were a spare tire that slid out from under the trunk on a tray, and a vast array of instruments (each with its own supplemental warning light) set in an oriental-wood dashboard. Though it weighed nearly 4000 pounds, the Gaylord behaved like a sports machine half as light. Top speed was 120 mph, and 60 mph came up in less than 10 seconds from a standstill. The fine chassis enabled smooth tracking through all kinds of bends.

Ultimately, the Gaylord was a dismal failure. A fabulous dream car, it presented the brothers with a dilemma. Jim was a perfectionist, satisfied with nothing less than exactly what he had planned. Quality on the first two pilot cars built didn't suit him. This led the company into a dispute with the builders, Luftschiffbau Zeppelin of Freidreichshaven, who had taken on the job in 1956 after Spohn built the prototype. By early 1957 the Gaylord project was officially dead.

Rear-end styling was typical 1950s: fins and lots of chrome.

Only four chassis were completed, one of which—with various components beautifully color-coded—is today on display along with a finished car at the Early American Museum in Orlando, Florida. Another chassis, which apparently once had a body, was last seen in Germany, but its fate is now unknown.

In retrospect, the main fault with the Gaylord enterprise was lack of solid production planning, something both brothers admit today. It is always easy to look back, of course. What nobody can take away from them is that the brilliantly designed Gaylord chassis was virtually unbreakable and worthy of any sports car ever built. The styling suffered from contemporary fads like excess chrome and funny tailfins, but the basic body design was original and exciting. Remove the fins, the wraparound windshield, the fancy wheel covers, and the needless chrome, and you're left with a shape that still looks good today. It's too bad the Gaylords had to give up before more cars were made.

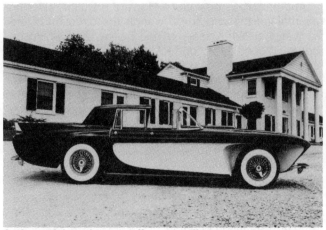

Scale-model roadster was "stretched" by retouching photo to create a four-door town car.

Here's the original prototype, photographed in Paris where it was first shown.

Henry Js That Weren't:
The Best Were Yet To Come

The Henry J was introduced by Kaiser-Frazer in early 1950 as a '51 model. It was one of America's pioneer postwar compacts—the second to appear after the Nash Rambler. It was also the car that kept Henry J. Kaiser's shaky automotive empire alive after the serious losses of 1949. Because of his promise to build a car all Americans could afford to buy new, Kaiser borrowed $69 million from the Reconstruction Finance Corporation in 1949. While $25 million of that was used to finance the firm's heavy 1949 inventories, the government okayed the deal mainly because some $12 million was earmarked for the new compact.

The Henry J debuted promising not just a low price but low running costs, too—and it delivered on both counts. But it sold for only a little less than a standard Ford or Chevy, which put it in a tough league, indeed. Production dipped after some 80,000 of the '51 models were built, falling to an 1123-unit trickle for 1954.

While the euphoria lasted, though, K-F designers harbored great plans for the Henry J. Its 100-inch-wheelbase chassis was a natural for a sports model. The Kaiser-Darrin and the Excalibur J two-seaters were both based on Henry J components. The company wanted to build a convertible and a hardtop itself. Several designs for Henry J derivatives were created. K-F never got these into production, though a few dealers built customized convertibles by chopping the tops off standard two-doors. A four-door sedan

(with a rear door that would have been trouble for anyone larger than a child to squeeze through) and a station wagon were also proposed—and abandoned.

Had the Henry J been more of a success, its first redesign would have come in 1955. The plan for the all-new second-generation model was first laid down in 1950, when sales were still high and management optimistic. According to former K-F managers and company documents, this car was part of a four- or five-year styling cycle that would have brought the Henry J up to 1960. The target wheelbases were 108.5 and 105 inches.

The most radical 1955 proposal centered around the 105-inch wheelbase and was created by Alex Tremulis, who was also involved with the wartime Chryslers, the Tucker, and the Gaylord. Tremulis had always been a champion of streamlining, and felt it was the key to a revolutionary new Henry J. Had this car been built, he might have been proved right. Named for its wheelbase, Tremulis' design was code-named the Kaiser "105."

"Our proposal was between the Henry J and Kaiser-Darrin in size, but with its lightness and small frontal area it could outperform both," Tremulis said. "We figured it to return 25 mpg and yield an estimated top speed of over 100 mph. The weight was only 2500 pounds. It was another Tucker—years ahead in concept and function. If it had been produced, in my opinion, there would have been a Big Four."

The "105" was a pretty little two-door coupe with broad areas of glass and a forward-thrusting front end, sharply cut back underneath for efficient airflow. Despite a mere five-inch gain in wheelbase over the original Henry J, it offered enormous increases in interior leg- and headroom.

Another K-F designer, Howard "Dutch" Darrin, maintained the way to go was in the direction of the sensational '51 Kaiser he had styled, and which he naturally considered perfect. As a companion to that car, he favored a Kaiser-like Henry J on a 100-inch wheelbase. Darrin actually built one at his Santa Monica, California studios, cutting 18 inches out of a Kaiser club coupe chassis and shortening the body panels appropriately. Like the '51 Kaiser, this was a lovely car, far better than what was actually produced. But at the time (1948), management felt that the Henry J should be "new" (in other words, different), and went ahead with what became the production '51 model.

Darrin never stopped pushing for his own Henry J, and some clay models were actually done up after regular production began. But his hopes were dashed. By 1953, the Henry J was going under, and K-F with it.

Tremulis' Kaiser 105 proposal might have been the '55 Henry J.

The production '51 would have looked like this had K-F listened to Darrin.

Hudson's Own '55:

It Wouldn't Have Been a "Hash"

Hudson probably wouldn't have survived had it not merged with Nash to form American Motors in 1954. Management had gone broke trying to sell six-cylinder Hornets in a V-8 market and compact Jets against 18-foot-long chrome cruisers. Had events been different, though, Hudson would have restyled completely for 1955, and might also have introduced its own V-8. These stillborn plans were based on the intriguing Italia and a four-door derivative labeled X-161.

The Italia was conceived by Hudson's innovative chief designer Frank Spring, and 26 semi-production examples were built under contract by Carozzeria Touring in Milan, Italy. Like the bulky '54 Hudsons, the Italia used a "Step-down" unit body, but sat nearly 10 inches lower. More importantly, it looked ultra-modern and entirely different. All the Italias were powered by an off-the-shelf engine, the 114-bhp six from the Jet. Wheelbase was the same practical 105 inches used for the dumpy compact, but the styling was unlike anything ever seen before from the Hudson Motor Car Company.

The Italia wore a wraparound windshield, matching GM's styling lead. Front fender scoops ducted cool air to the front brakes, and intakes along the bodysides did the same for the rear brakes. The rear end was a mite overstyled, with a vertical bank of three chrome-plated tubes on each side. These looked like exhaust pipes, but really housed the tail, directional, and backup

lights. Borrani wire wheels completed the package. The most common exterior color for the aluminum body was light cream.

The interior was revolutionary. Doors were cut 14 inches into the roof to allow easy entry and exit. There was a vast amount of room for passengers who sat on "anatomical" seats of unique design, and which were upholstered in red-and-white leather. Flow-through ventilation, the first in the American industry, was provided via cowl air intakes and exhaust grooves at the top of the rear windows. Spring claimed that the air inside an Italia changed completely every 10 minutes.

Coachbuilder Touring had little influence over the car's design. In the same way Ghia served Chrysler, Touring provided Hudson with expertise in low-volume production. Hudson called the shots, and made many changes after the initial prototype was built. This first car had a 100-inch wheelbase, a special dash, Alfa-Romeo steering wheel, full-leather upholstery, and a die-cast grille. Later specimens were "prodified" with Jet instruments and wheel, leather-and-vinyl upholstery, and stamped grilles.

Hudson hinted the Italia might become more than just an interesting limited-production two-seater. The company referred to it as "a family car with undreamed-of styling, luxury, and comfort."

The first prototype was used to test the waters at U.S auto shows. On the strength of its reception, Hudson ordered 25 additional 105-inch-wheelbase cars, and

Hudson's Own '55

set the Italia's retail price at $4800.

Unfortunately, even these few examples didn't sell well (many had to be retitled as 1955s). There were several reasons. The price was high, for one thing. For another, the Italia performed no better than the lowly Jet. Compared to the '54 Corvette's 0-60 mph time of 11 seconds and 106-mph top speed, for example, the Italia took 15 seconds to reach 60, topped out at just 95 mph, and cost $1300 more. The Italian-made body was also, apparently, very loose. According to chief engineer Stuart Baits, "When you drove it you'd think it was just going to fall apart."

Many of the Italia's faults could probably have been cured in mass production. Volume cars would have cost less, performed better, and with Detroit-built steel bodies would have proved more durable. Frank Spring had every confidence in the car's overall design. Even while the Italia coupes were being built, he was working on the next logical step: a full-size, 124-inch-wheelbase four-door called X-161.

The X-161 had all the Italia's features—cut-in doors, cooling vents, and the low profile, Step-down frame—but instead of the Jet engine, it was powered by the Hornet's 170-bhp six. This mighty 306-cid powerhouse had proven its worth in stock-car racing. The only problem was that most people wanted V-8s in those days. Several former Hudson managers have suggested that, by 1955, the Hornet engine would have

been joined by a V-8. Though Hudson itself was not actively working on one, there were several proprietary units available. Packard, for example, was suffering from excess engine production capacity at the time, and would have welcomed the extra business. It's not hard to imagine the kind of performance the Hudson would have had with 352 cubic inches of Packard V-8 under the hood.

Also worth noting, the X-161 was, in some respects, like the contemporary Nash, which was decorated with certain Italia-like features to become the 1955-57 Hudson. It had the same taut, rounded look, the same window frames, and the same good visibility. Roy D. Chapin, Jr., son of a Hudson founder and later AMC president, was a Hudson sales manager in those days: "That X-161 . . . was an absolute knock-out, just like the Italia only with four doors. I got a laugh when Dick Teague [AMC chief stylist] proposed a four-door Javelin in 1970 for the ongoing Ambassador or Matador. I said, 'History's repeating itself.' [The X-161] is dated—but it's still a terrific exercise in automotive design. But again the problem with it was much the same with the other cars in the lineup. It was a very costly car to make and couldn't command the price you had to get for it, coupled with the fact that the decision was made to put nothing but a six-cylinder engine in it."

Had the 1955 Hudson line been built around X-161 concepts with either a Hudson-made or proprietary V-8, chances are that the make's fortunes would have turned out better than they did. American Motors sold just 20,000 of the Nash-based '55 models. Hudson vanished after 1957.

Gimmicky triple "exhaust pipes" housed rear lights.

Scoops above headlights cooled front brakes.

"Production" Italias had Jet instruments and steering wheel.

Detractors called the Nash-based '55 Hudson a "Hash."

Pirana:

A Once-in-a-Lifetime Jaguar

Six years after the sensational Jaguar E-Type had been launched, a unique custom-bodied version was displayed at the London and Turin Motor Shows. Called the Pirana, it was strictly a "one-off" prototype built by Bertone, and never saw even limited production. In fact, after its brief show appearances in the autumn of 1967, the car was rarely seen again. It was never road tested, and, for a time, seemed to have vanished completely.

Other styling houses had tried to improve the E-Type's smooth lines. All the attempts had failed, and none had had the blessing of Jaguar's Sir William Lyons. In this respect, at least, the Bertone project was different. Of course, Jaguar was not looking around for new styling: there was no need to change. E-Type demand continued to exceed supply, as it had right from the start. The Pirana came about because the *Daily Telegraph Magazine* was looking for some publicity. It's actually quite a complicated story.

The Geneva Motor Show of March 1967 was a glittering occasion graced by show cars based on Ferrari, Maserati, Lamborghini, and other Italian "supercar" chassis. The *Daily Telegraph's* motoring correspondent, Courtenay Edwards, and the editor of the *Magazine,* John Anstey, drifted into one of those conversations that always begin with "Isn't it a pity that . . ." They wondered why none of the gloriously styled dream pieces on display there were derived from a British model. From there, it was only a short step to the idea that *if* a suitable British chassis were available, and *if* an Italian coachmaker would build a show car, then perhaps the *Daily Telegraph Magazine* could find a way to pay for it all. The car would be a publicity vehicle, of course.

Anstey, who ran the magazine in much the same way a medieval baron ran his estates, was so fired up by the notion that he pushed ahead with it. The understanding was that the finished car should be ready by October. Eight months to build a complete car—not merely an empty shell, but a completely functional prototype—was a tall order, even for the large and reputable concerns that were to be involved. Anstey's brief was not only that the car look beautiful, but also that it be designed around a British production chassis. Naturally, it should incorporate all the latest safety, comfort, and performance features. But most of all, it had to be an *all-British* blend of speed, luxury, and style.

All, that is, except the styling, which (almost inevitably) had to be assigned to an Italian *carrozzerie.* At that time, virtually no British coachbuilder had established the sort of international reputation Anstey thought suitable for such a prestigious project. Several Italian styling houses, no doubt, could have done a good job in the available time. But Bertone's reputation was even higher than that of the others, so the Turin bodybuilder got the contract.

Choosing the car's mechanical base was easy. Jaguar's E-Type was far and away the fastest and the most successful British design available. (The only real alternative was the Aston Martin DB6, but it was known to be on the way out—to be replaced by the new DBS, launched later in the year.) To give Bertone as much creative working room as possible, it was decided the long-wheelbase chassis from the 2+2 model (introduced in the spring of 1966) should be used.

By the end of April 1967, the basic design had been settled. Jaguar agreed to sell a 2+2 E-Type chassis to the *Daily Telegraph Magazine;* Nuccio Bertone agreed to accept the commission. The target completion date was mid-October, in time for the Earls Court Show. The car was to be called the Jaguar "Pirana." (The spelling deliberately differs from that of the ferocious South American fish, perhaps for some obscure trademark reason.)

Bertone and his chief designer Marcello Gandini were given a free hand in shaping the Pirana, although for reasons of practicality and chic, it had to be a

Pirana

closed coupe. Despite the use of the longer 2+2 chassis, the car was conceived as a two-seater—no more and no less. The "free hand," incidentally, did not extend to the mechanical layout, which was supposed to stay virtually unaltered. Compared with the production 2+2 E-Type, the only significant chassis change for the Pirana was that wide-rim center-lock wheels (not unlike those of the famous D-Type) and Dunlop racing tires were fitted.

Although Jaguar always made it clear that it was not interested in a possible new production design (Sir William, together with aerodynamicist Malcolm Sayer, did all Jaguar styling himself), the firm actively encouraged the project. Bob Berry, the company's executive director of publicity, made several visits to Turin (along with Anstey and Courtenay Edwards) to check on the car's progress. The company was also invaluable for help in obtaining special items for the handmade shell.

It's very easy to talk about using the E-Type "chassis," but it was by no means easy for Jaguar to supply one. The E-Type, after all, had a multi-tubular front chassis, but the center and tail sections of the fastback coupe were a pressed-steel monocoque. Therefore, Jaguar delivered a half-built car to Bertone without superstructure, doors, windshield, or outer panels. For structural reasons, the standard underframe, sills, and rear wheel arches were retained.

Despite this, Bertone did a magnificent job. As it turned out, the Pirana had a striking resemblance to the four-place Lamborghini Espada, a production model that Bertone was developing at the same time. And it's almost impossible for a designer not to let ideas and influences overlap among different projects.

The Pirana's long, very sleek lines were emphasized by a seemingly endless hood. The nose, though, was very bluff, and carried a full-width grille with four headlamps. The sloping fastback roof ended rather abruptly in a square tail much like that of the contemporary Ford Mustang. Like the standard E-Type, the Pirana's hood and front fenders formed a single unit that hinged at the front. Because it had only two seats and the same wheelbase, the Pirana had a more spacious interior than the 2+2 Jaguar. Although the standard car had a hatchback-cum-rear window hinged at the side, Bertone's design made do with a large top-hinged rear window. Below this was a vertical glass pane in the tail panel, hidden by louvers.

Special fittings included experimental Triplex "Sundym" glass with a vinyl interlayer in the windshield, and electric defroster wires embedded in the rear window. Both these features have since been adopted by many production cars. A Smiths air-conditioning system was used in place of the Jaguar's feeble standard heater.

Although the Pirana looked larger than the production Jaguar, it was actually four inches shorter, 0.7-inch wider, and marginally lower. As a handbuilt show car, it was inevitably somewhat heavier than the standard product. A look at the sumptuous interior appointments showed where some of that weight had been added. There were large and squashy reclining seats, a more comprehensive instrument display, and extra luxury details. The entire body was fashioned in steel, except for the hood, which was made of light-alloy. The acrylic silver finish contained minute particles of aluminum.

The Pirana was unveiled just two days before the London Motor Show opened its doors. At that point, it had not been driven on the road. Although visually stunning, the car later proved to have poor aerodynamics and disappointing performance. After its show appearances, it was auctioned off in North America in 1968 and had several owners over the next few years. Today, it is back in Britain. It had done its job for the *Daily Telegraph Magazine,* and remains a Jaguar that should have been.

Built on the E-Type 2+2 chassis, the Pirana featured a glass tail panel like that on Bertone's 1966 Lamborghini Marzal show car. Hood and top of front fenders were hinged as a unit as on the Jaguar.

Kaiser-Frazer:
New Styles That Didn't Make It

The 1952 Frazer and the 1956 Kaiser did exist—and not just on paper. But neither ever reached the showrooms. Inept management policy in the case of the Frazer, and company reverses in the case of the Kaiser, were the reasons.

The Kaiser-Frazer combine had been created in 1945. It was an unholy alliance between Joseph W. Frazer, president of Graham-Paige, and Henry J. Kaiser, the tycoon builder of Liberty and Victory ships, dams, and factories. Frazer wanted to get back into the auto industry after the war, but lacked the money. Kaiser had the money and also wanted to build cars, but lacked the know-how. Kaiser saw Frazer as a means, however temporary, for learning the ropes of

the car business. Soon after the company was formed, Kaiser's managers started replacing people hired by Frazer. By 1949, Henry J. controlled everything from the boardroom to the assembly lines.

It was Kaiser's personal power that led—over Joe Frazer's objections—to the decision to tool up for 200,000 cars in 1949. Frazer's opposition was based on his long experience in the industry. The 1949 K-F cars were mere facelifts, while rival Big-Three models were brand-new designs. Frazer voted to pull back by building fewer cars than the year before, then make a comeback with the all-new line being readied for 1950. In a memorable board meeting in early 1949, Henry told his partner, "the Kaisers never retrench." In

First Frazer freshening would have come in '52. This is Herb Weissinger's adaptation of "Dutch" Darrin's '51 Kaiser bodyshell.

Kaiser-Frazer

protest Frazer resigned as president (Kaiser was chairman), and Henry appointed his son Edgar to take over for Frazer. K-F went after 200,000 cars, sold 60,000, and took a loss of $30.3 million—then, one of the largest amounts ever lost by an auto firm of that size.

The striking new 1951 Kaiser was originally planned as a '50 model, but was set back six months by the pileup of unsold '49s. These were slowly moved out by selling them at big discounts; some were reserialed as "1950" models. About 10,000 were transformed into 1951 Frazers by means of a facelift from the cowl forward and from the deck backwards. All this caused the rakish new 118-inch-wheelbase sedans originally scheduled for introduction in the autumn of 1949 to be delayed until spring 1950. By this time, K-F had already reserialed a few cars as 1950 models, so it was logical to call the new design a '51, giving it a six-month jump on the competition.

The 1951 Kaiser/Frazer had been designed in 1949. Basically, it was the work of styling consultant Howard A. "Dutch" Darrin, who successfully campaigned his clay model against those of K-F's in-house design team and Brooks Stevens, another consultant. Certain details on the approved production version, such as

Another '52 Frazer proposal was this convertible styled by Cliff Voss who later went to Chrysler. Note the "sweetheart dip" windshield header.

Lack of finances prevented Kaiser from getting this hardtop into production. Stylist Alex Tremulis dubbed it "Sun Goddess."

bumpers, hood ornament, and grille, were worked out by K-F Styling's Herb Weissinger and Arnott B. "Buzz" Grisinger. But the long, low shape was all Darrin's. Beautiful and different, it was a good five years ahead of anything else in Detroit. It wasn't until the 1957 Chrysler products came along that an American production car would have such a low beltline.

J. W. Frazer and the Frazer nameplate were still intrinsic parts of the corporation when the '51 Kaiser was being designed, so there were also plans for a Frazer version. As with the 1947-48 program, the Frazer would have been continued as a more luxurious and costlier Kaiser. With the pile-up of 1949 models and the interim '51 facelift, an all-new Darrin-based

Frazer was put off until the 1952 model year.

Styled by Herb Weissinger, this car would have had a complex eggcrate grille, placed low down and closely integrated with the front bumper. Weissinger and his colleagues tried numerous sketches, two of which are shown here. Toward 1949, after the face-lifted '51 Frazer was in the works, he toyed with putting its grille on Darrin's Kaiser bodyshell. But this was as far as it went. With Joe Frazer reduced to the meaningless position of board vice-chairman, management saw no need for a separate Frazer line. By 1953, Kaiser-Frazer Corporation had been renamed Kaiser Motors, Inc.

The Darrin-styled 1951 Kaiser went through several

Darrin came up with this modest trim variation as a facelift for the 1960 Argentine Carabela. Body is basically unchanged from the 1951 U.S. original.

Kaiser-Frazer

facelifts in the early '50s. While company fortunes were still high, there were plans to develop several new body styles from the sedan, including a hardtop and a convertible. One hardtop prototype, dubbed "Sun Goddess" by stylist Alex Tremulis, was actually constructed from a '51 two-door sedan. Basically stock from the beltline down, it carried a glamorous pillarless coupe roof with a broadly wrapped backlight. This car survives today in the hands of a Pacific Coast collector.

Due mainly to its lack of a V-8 engine, Kaiser did not sell well after 1951. Accordingly, the company postponed development of hardtops or convertibles, and relied mainly on facelifts to make its sedan look "different" year after year. These annual trim changes had some remarkably pleasing results. By 1954, the '51 body had acquired a distinctive concave grille, a wraparound rear window, and three-sided teardrop taillights with supplementary red lenses running up along the tops of the fenders.

Had fortunes been different, Kaiser Motors would have completely restyled for 1956, based on an all-new design not unlike the one proposed for the '56 Henry J (see Chapter 16) on a longer 118-inch wheelbase. But with sales tapering off to 20,000 or 30,000 a year and red ink flowing, the company simply couldn't afford it. In early 1955, management decided to abandon the passenger-car market and concentrate strictly on Jeep vehicles. The very last, half-hearted proposal for a Kaiser facelift was a garish, two-toned '54 model. To the dismay of no one, it was never produced.

But the Kaiser nameplate was far from dead. The indefatigable Henry Kaiser had no sooner given up on America when he was down in Argentina, negotiating with dictator Juan Peron for the founding of a local auto company. This became Industrias Kaiser Argentina AS (IKA), and was under the direction of James McCloud, brother-in-law of Henry's son Edgar.

Just before the end, the production '54 Kaiser Manhattan wore a pretty nifty facelift of a four-year-old design...

...but later facelifts would have ruined the car's basically clean lines. This nightmare was an idea for '55.

68

James Anger of the Toledo design staff contemplated a new squared-off roofline grafted on top of the Kaiser's curvaceous lower body.

From 1958 through 1962, an Argentine version of the 1954-55 Manhattan called the Kaiser "Carabela" (Caravelle, the ship) was produced at the rate of about 3000 units a year. The Carabela was basically identical to the earlier American model, and used the same 226-cid flathead six-cylinder engine. Unlike the 1954-55 Manhattan, the Carabela was normally aspirated (a supercharger wasn't offered), and had 115 bhp. The suspension was toughened to handle rough Argentine roads, and the only transmission available was a three-speed manual.

It is a tribute to the original Darrin styling that the Manhattan/Carabela lasted as long as it did. It might have gone on even longer, for there were some ideas brewing as late as 1960 to keep it up to date. In that year, the imaginative Darrin was asked to come up with a facelift for the Carabela. He produced two models, one conservative, the other more radical. The "mild" version was a near-copy of the production model. It differed only by having a modest scoop-type windshield header, ponderous moldings on front fenders and doors, and a full-length chrome strip running from the front wheel well back through the rear fender. Darrin built this proposal on an early 1954 Kaiser Special (which lacked the wraparound rear window).

The more ambitious facelift would have looked very nice, indeed. A reskinning from the cowl forward, it would have involved replacing all sheetmetal ahead of the firewall with a low, sloping hoodline that dropped down to a narrow grille opening. Above the front bumper was a simple bar grille flanked by quad headlights. This model was favorably received by management, but it was ultimately decided that pro-

duction levels in Argentina didn't warrant the tooling required.

But Kaiser wasn't dead yet. Back in Toledo, Ohio, where Henry Kaiser had repaired to build Jeeps after selling the old Willow Run, Michigan factory, James Anger of the Production Development staff was at work. Anger thought the only thing on the Carabela that needed updating was its superstructure. He envisioned shearing off the roof and replacing it with a modern, squared-off style somewhat like that of the early-'60s Lincoln Continentals. Anger actually constructed a prototype from the bottom of an old Manhattan sedan, using fiberglass for the new roof and plexiglass for the side windows. Although the result was an aesthetic mis-match—squared-off roofline resting on a curved, rounded body—it didn't look too bad. A considerable increase in glass area was achieved, although the original roof design had been good in this respect.

Eventually, all these "extensions" of the '54 Kaiser went by the boards for the same reason: insufficient sales volume to justify tooling costs. By 1962, the old Manhattan/Carabela dies were worn out, and the car was dropped in Argentina. In its place, IKA first adopted the old Alfa Romeo body for a 1962-64 crib called the "Bergantine" (Brigantine). Then it tried a facelifted version of the 1964 Rambler American, called it the Torino, and had good success. In fact, that car was still in production in 1980. IKA later built Renaults under license, and made quite a name for itself in South America. Ultimately, it was taken over completely by Renault. Henry Kaiser sold his interests to the locals in 1965.

The Postwar LaSalle:
A Never-Was That Might Yet Be

It isn't hard to explain the failure of the first LaSalles, those classic beauties of 1927-33: the Depression was the cause. After 1931, luxury cars simply didn't sell well. Several companies that depended solely on expensive models disappeared. It's harder to explain why GM dropped LaSalle for 1941 after a number of good years as an upper-medium-price car in the late '30s. But there *was* a reason—a logical one. Toward the end, the lower-priced Cadillacs, the LaSalle, and the more costly Buicks had become very much alike. By 1940, the LaSalle Model 52 and the Cadillac 62 were nearly identical in form, finish, body style offerings, and performance. LaSalle was extremely close to Buick in price. It didn't make

sense for GM to continue LaSalle as a rival to these better-established makes.

There was another reason for LaSalle's demise. The economy was recovering in the years just before Pearl Harbor, and Cadillac had made a strategic decision that would take it to the pinnacle of its field after the war. The division chose to stop competing in the upper-medium-price market. Packard, which continued to offer a cheaper companion line after the war, eventually lost its golden name and, as one ex-Packard executive put it, "handed the luxury market to Cadillac on a silver platter."

This fastback sedan was one of two prototypes for the stillborn '41 LaSalle. Styling was typical of GM for the period.

manner of the Cadillac 60 Special, and the rear fenders fashionably skirted. Two 1941 LaSalle prototypes were built—a fastback four-door sedan, and a notchback four-door. With the decision to axe the line, the Cadillac 61, comparable in size and price, was moved in to replace LaSalle—but not for long. Cadillac moved even more decisively toward the high-price sector, and abandoned the 61 after 1951.

In spite of LaSalle's historic role as Cadillac's less expensive companion, it was hard to lose the car; many at GM remembered it warmly for years afterward. The 1927 LaSalle, after all, had brought Harley Earl to General Motors where he set up the famed Art & Colour Studio. The '34 model was far less prestigious than previous LaSalles, but was remembered for its rather daring styling instead of it's middling price tag. And the name itself had a certain panache: French-sounding enough to be snooty, but with a history that was 100-percent American. Stylists are romantic folk, and over the years GM designers had visions of LaSalle's eventual return as a sort of exclusive two- or four-seat Cadillac.

Harley Earl was probably GM's greatest romantic of all, so when two special show cars were required for the 1955 Motorama, it wasn't surprising that he dubbed them "LaSalle." And that wasn't all: both had the 1940-41 style vertical grille openings, and wore the original "LaS" emblems used in the make's last years. Earl called both these cars LaSalle II.

One was an open model, a two-seat roadster of the Corvette stripe, with concave side sculpture that prefigured that of the 1956 'Vette. An interesting detail was its open rear fender design, not unlike the concept Brooks Stevens used at the front wheels of the stillborn Gaylord (see Chapter 15).

The other LaSalle II was a four-door hardtop with rear-hinged back doors, like those on Earl's forthcoming Cadillac Eldorado Brougham. Though it seated six,

GM stylists, of course, had been planning the '41 models long before higher management made that decision, so there *was* a '41 LaSalle in the works. This would have been a mild revision of the lovely 1940 design, retaining the by-then traditional, narrow horizontal-bar grille, flanked by prominent vertical openings in the front fender aprons. Headlights set into the fenders were retained. The profile was pure General Motors, with the front fenders squared off in the

Notchback '41 proposal carried Cadillac-style taillights, and rear fender trim. "52" was LaSalle's series number.

Slim LaSalle nose and "catwalk" air intakes would have continued on the '41s. Oblong parking lights were new.

The '55 LaSalle II hardtop sedan show car featured prewar styling themes up front, including original LaSalle emblem.

The Postwar LaSalle

the LaSalle hardtop had a compact, 108-inch wheelbase, was only 180 inches long, and stood just 50 inches off the ground. That lowness was partly achieved by using 13-inch tires—quite rare for any Detroit car, even show cars, in 1955. GM described this car as "a new concept of passenger sedan styling directed to recapture the distinctive exclusiveness and high quality of craftsmanship of the original LaSalle." But to many it just looked silly. It did predict some future trends, though. The floor, body sills, engine supports, and bodyshell were fused into an integrated whole. The sills formed main structural members, and also served to house the exhaust pipe and muffler.

Strictly Motorama cars, both LaSalle IIs were never intended to reach your local dealer. But the name surfaced again in the early '60s, with production definitely in mind. This was the project that culminated in the 1963 Buick Riviera. Originally, the thought was to launch this hardtop Thunderbird-beater as a personal-luxury Cadillac called LaSalle. But Buick's poor sales in the early part of the decade dictated some additional product help, so the car was assigned to Flint. With this change the first real chance since 1940 for a re-born LaSalle was lost.

In the early '70s, Cadillac again thought seriously about using the LaSalle name for the new small sedan that ultimately became the Seville. The choice was virtually assured until one division executive came across an article that characterized the original LaSalle as "Cadillac's only failure." Unknowingly, the writer helped prevent the return of one of his favorite nameplates.

But they still talk about LaSalles in Detroit—and one name they're talking about for a future Cadillac compact is . . . "LaSalle." We haven't reached the end of the story just yet. It may have been a car that never was in the past, but a new LaSalle might just be in store for the future.

This swanky-looking coupe might have had the LaSalle label. This clay wore Cadillac emblems, but led to Buick Riviera.

Replacements for the MGB:

Triumphs Were the Corporate Will

The first MGB rolled off the line at Abingdon, England (near Oxford) back in 1962. The last one was scheduled to be built in the autumn of 1980. Apart from minor interior and exterior changes over its 18-year production life, the B stayed remarkably the same. But MG certainly didn't plan it that way. On at least two occasions, the designers laid out plans for replacements—and were turned down by higher authority. Company policy ensured the B's lack of change, which, in the end, helped kill off the MG name.

A word about corporate structure. Since 1935, MG had been part of the Nuffield Group, which became the British Motor Corporation (BMC) in 1952. After a series of complex deals, BMC merged with Leyland Motors to form British Leyland in 1968, and it was BL that finally sunk MG. In 45 years, MG never had the freedom to design and develop its own cars; it always had to fit in with somebody's corporate product plans (when they existed). After 1968, MG had to compete for funds or

financial favors with Triumph, the "other" sports car maker in the BL stable. Triumph had been acquired by Leyland in 1961, and Leyland executives had dominated BL since its formation. That's probably why MG was so neglected in the '70s in favor of new Triumph models like the TR6 and TR7.

The MGB was conceived in 1959-60 as a successor to the MGA, then five years into a seven-year production life. It went on sale in September 1962, with a modified BMC engine, gearbox, and rear axle; the MGA's independent front suspension; and a steel unit body/chassis built by Pressed Steel Ltd. If that hodge-podge of parts sounds like some General Motors cars, remember that BMC was the British equivalent of GM in those days, so original design always took a back seat to production convenience. John Thornley, MG's general manager at the time, once said that he always thought the MGB would be the last completely new steel-bodied car built at

73

Replacements for the MGB

Abingdon because its tooling costs seemed so enormous. He would be proved right, but was also very sad about it.

By 1967 (significantly, while it was still a separate company) BMC had sold over 100,000 MGBs, with about 600 a week being produced. A design team now started creating a successor to the five-year-old B. The new model was scheduled to go on sale in 1970.

The project that began to evolve carried the code designation EX234 (EX for experimental, project 234). This was seen as a replacement not only for the middle-range B, but also for the smaller, lower-priced MG Midget/Austin-Healey Sprite, which dated back to 1958. With that in mind, the designers aimed for something more compact and stylish than the MGB. The new model would be based on existing engines and transmissions—the "building-block" philosophy so well-developed by GM. One version would be offered with the 1275cc Midget powerplant and gearbox, while the 1798cc MGB drivetrain would be used for the more expensive model. Automatic transmission, which first appeared as an option for the B Mk II of 1967-68, would be available with the larger engine only.

EX234's open sports body was a conventional pressed-steel monocoque with integral chassis. Although it was no larger physically than the existing MGB, it would be a genuine 2+2 instead of only a two-seater. Wheelbase was shorter—87 inches compared to the B's 91 inches—and its passenger compartment was set farther forward in relation to overall length.

At the time, BMC wanted all its new models to use the rubber-and-liquid "Hydrolastic" suspension units first seen on the Morris 1100 of 1962. Later adopted for the Mini and the Austin/Morris 1800, this system was

seen in the U.S. on the MG 1100, Vanden Plas Princess, and Austin America sedans of the late 1960s, where—as in England—it was not a success. Hydrolastic was an all-independent system, with interconnected front and rear "spring" units on each side. With a great deal more effort it could have been adapted to provide self-leveling. Its biggest drawbacks were its complexity and poor reliability. Nevertheless, it was loyally picked up for the new MG, allied to a wishbone front linkage and semi-trailing wishbones at the rear. The differential casing, which had to be fixed to the monocoque, was taken from the four-wheel-drive Austin Gipsy. Wheels were to be 12 inches in diameter for the small-engine model, and 13 inches with the larger engine (The MGB had 14-inch road wheels).

Styling for EX234 was done by the Italian house of Pininfarina, which had been under contract to BMC for some years. A prototype rolling chassis was shipped off to Italy and returned as a complete car in 1968. The body was quite attractive, even for a PF design. It offered a very good seating package and even managed to retain a family resemblance to the existing MGB, with just a hint of Pininfarina's sumptuous Ferrari styling.

EX234 was almost too good to be true, and there's little doubt MG would have liked to get it in production. The prototype's level of interior trim was thought to be a bit lavish for the rigid cost targets that had been set (Hydrolastic was also very costly). With its sloping nose and compact engine bay, the EX234 would not accept the long 2912cc inline six that had just been introduced for the MGC. But no one worried much about that, as the shortcomings of the supposed successor to the Austin-Healey 3000 were already too apparent. It was also clear that Hydrolastic was not very satisfactory. But "son of Hydrolastic"—called Hydragas—was on the way and promised improved ride and handling. All that remained to be done was to settle on certain exterior trim items and possibly a fastback coupe version. Pininfarina was not asked to develop a closed body style, but did not see adapting the roadster to fastback form as a problem.

Despite all this, EX234 was abandoned in 1968. It wasn't because of the design, or the financial implications of tooling up for it. It was simply because the project was completed at about the time BMC merged with Leyland. Corporate planning was disrupted, as the problem of overlapping and duplicating models in the combined product lines was discussed. Another factor was the American safety and exhaust-emission regulations that had been enacted since the project started. BL executives weren't sure whether to "keep the MGB legal" or redesign EX234 to comply with these new requirements: the company couldn't afford to do both. EX234 was accordingly dropped, and the B was left to soldier on.

Two years later, the confusion caused by the 1968 merger was being resolved, and the question of an MGB replacement came up again. In an effort to come up with the right sports car for the mid-1970s, BL set up

Cockpit would have permitted 2+2 seating.

Styled by Pininfarina, EX234 would have been a strong rival to Fiat's 124 Sport Spider in the late '60s.

a sort of design competition between MG and Triumph. Triumph was asked to work up proposals for a new front-engine model (which eventually became the TR7), while MG was asked to develop a mid-engine car. Development of the MG prototype began in 1970 under the project code ADO21 (ADO for Austin Drawing Office, project number 21) indicating it was a corporate effort.

Low-price mid-engine sports cars were all the rage in the late '60s, especially after the Lotus Europa appeared in 1967, followed by the Porsche 914 in 1969. Once again, the designers on the ADO21 were told to use as many off-the-shelf components as possible, but had more latitude in suspension design than with EX234. They soon realized that the mid-

engine layout dictated a two-seater. They also decided the car would have to be a fixed-roof coupe to satisfy present and proposed U.S. legislation. This made it almost inevitable that the basic shape would be a wedge derivative as adopted on many European models in recent years.

Because ADO21's mid-engine layout would require a combined engine/gearbox/final-drive assembly, it made sense to use one already in production. The choice was obvious: BL's ohc E-series engines, four-cylinder and six-cylinder units of 1798cc and 2227cc, respectively. These were already used in the front-drive Austin Maxi sedan, and were engineered for transverse installation with five-speed gearboxes and spur-gear final drives. The only major problem in the

Left side of EX234 prototype lacked the side molding used on the right. The car is still occasionally seen today.

Replacements for the MGB

ADO21 was that the gear linkage would have to come out through the front of the transmission casing instead of the rear.

The wedge-style coupe was ready for approval in November 1970. It featured a long and sharply detailed nose, a squat Europa-like rear deck, and engine air intakes located on the lower bodysides behind the doors and ahead of the rear wheels. Although this was an entirely new style and mechanical layout for MG, the structure was designed as a conventional pressed-steel monocoque Because of the powertrain's bulk and midships location, a de Dion rear suspension was proposed, with the big tube behind the engine, single-leaf elliptic springs, and a Watts linkage for lateral location. Front suspension was by MacPherson strut, and designed to share parts with the then-developing TR7.

At this stage, there were many things to be resolved. This included the possibility of a larger engine (it was to be 2227cc for Britain, but an enlarged 2622cc unit was under development in Australia), and the radiator position (either in the nose or in the engine bay). Deciding where to put the fuel tank was difficult, but it probably would have been placed between the engine bay and the seats for impact protection.

Like EX234, ADO21 was cleverly conceived, but it, too, was canceled for only incidental reasons. BL management, led by Triumph advocates Donald Stokes and George Turnbull, decided in favor of the front-engine TR7. Unlike EX234, no running prototype of ADO21 was ever built; the only records of it that remain are the photographs of the clay model shown here and a few drawings. After this, the company gave up entirely on an MGB replacement—and ultimately on MG itself.

EX234, at least, still survives. Fitted with a 1275cc engine, it is occasionally seen in public as a poignant reminder of the MG that might have been.

The mid-engine ADO21 competed for company funds in 1970 with a front-engine Triumph proposal which eventually became the TR7.

Only this non-running mock-up of the mid-engine MG was built. Car would have been offered with four- or six-cylinder power.

Packard's Request:

The Revival of a Familiar Theme

Bringing back the classic radiator was a new idea in 1954. That's when Packard Styling began the program that produced the Request.

The '50s, of course, were years of bold chrome smiles, sheetmetal sculptures, and spaceship motifs. Styling themes of that era were supposed to emphasize a car's sheer size, because Detroit was firmly convinced that customers wanted each new model to be longer, lower, and wider than the one before it. Today we've gone the other way: the "classic" upright grille (preferably adorned with a stand-up hood ornament) is the fashion, and has become cliché. Its use on American cars came about because of its association with prestige makes like Rolls-Royce and Mercedes-Benz, both of which have used the same basic grille theme for many years. Daimler-Benz recently let it be known that it might cease using its trademark front. The news generated such a howl of protest from dealers that the company changed its mind. Obviously, dealers feel that formal grille is a sales-maker—and they're probably right.

Back in 1954, putting an old-style radiator on an American car seemed precisely the wrong thing to do. Everybody was looking ahead. But Packard had a special reason for looking back. Studebaker-Packard

president James J. Nance had swept into power in 1952 on a promise to rebuild Packard's squandered luxury image. He felt that reviving the make's traditional grille style would underline his intent. Nance said he had received numerous letters from Packard owners urging such a change, and claimed this showed it would have the effect he hoped for.

The distinctive Packard grille originated with the 1904 Model L, probably inspired by a similar design on the French Mors. Though the radiator grew, shrank, and got wider or higher as the car itself changed, the basic shape had been maintained through 1950. With the 1951 "Twenty-fourth" Series, a more open design appeared, though the peaked "cusps" of the past could still be seen in the "ox-yoke" upper grille. This grille outline was continued throughout the '50s, and even the last Studebaker-based Packards of 1957-58 retained it to some degree. But the shape was not as apparent as it once was, and Packard's sales people agreed they had lost an important marketing tool. It was late 1953 when Nance asked his styling department to come up with a modern rendition of the prewar theme. "I was trying to resurrect the traditional grille," he said, "which I thought was the real Packard trademark."

Packard's Request

Chief designer Richard A. Teague began by reworking the hood and front bumper of a 1953 Packard, using 1954 headlamp rims and a short, modern adaptation of the classic grille shape. Several different motifs were tried. But the production '54s were rushed out with only a minor facelift of the '53 look, instead of the major restyle that had been planned that year. So, Teague went on to work up an upright grille suitable for the 1955 line.

Nance continued to fire away at recapturing past glories, and even suggested a limited-production custom-bodied model designed by someone like Howard A. "Dutch" Darrin. The famous designer actually prepared such a car—a four-seat stretch of his Kaiser Darrin, with sliding doors that moved in two directions to allow access to either front or rear seat. This prototype displayed one of the most beautiful modern interpretations of the classic Packard grille ever executed, but lack of funds prevented it from reaching production.

After Teague completed the '55 production styling, he turned again to a classic-grilled special. This was slated for the Chicago Automobile Show in early 1955. He chose a Four Hundred hardtop, modified its hood, and installed large horizontal bumpers with the parking lights housed in large chrome bombs at the inner ends. Between these, square in the center, was a magnificent, upright classic radiator. In honor of all those Packard fanciers demanding just such a treatment, Teague named this car "The Request." Its serial number was 5587-1003.

Was the Request a prediction of production cars to come? Yes and no. It wasn't completed in time to influence 1955-56 styling (even as an optional altera-

A '54 Clipper was used for this Request-type grille. Front-end restyle for '55 kept it from production.

tion), but a narrower version of its traditional grille was to have been used on the all-new Packard scheduled for 1957 (see next chapter). Drawings for these models invariably featured the trademark grille as the dominant frontal motif—tall, graceful, pronounced. As we now know, sagging finances after the closure of Packard's Detroit plant caused the "real" 1957 Packard to be scrapped, replaced by Studebakers in Packard dress.

The one-off Request survived, however. It left the company sometime in 1957, and then just disappeared. For years enthusiasts wondered about its

Request was first shown at the 1955 Chicago Auto Show. This photo was taken after restoration in the mid-'70s.

Request was developed after the '55s were done. This ugly surgery, performed on a '54 model, wasn't accepted.

fate. Most assumed it had gone to the scrap heap, a forgotten and unwanted Detroit dream with a significance that was probably lost on the man with the blowtorch. But it didn't turn out that way. The Request was found rotting away quietly in an Oregon field by a Pacific Coast enthusiast in 1974. How it had come to the northwest was a mystery. But its new and sympathetic owner went right to work, evidently aware of its history. The photographs here were taken shortly after a full restoration was completed.

The rebuild took considerable effort. The interior was stripped and damaged bodywork repaired where needed. During the application of a new white-and-bronze paint job, three grille bars were recast and one bumper section was heli-arc'd. The chrome wire wheels with cloisonné Packard hubcap emblems were renewed, along with all exterior hardware, including the unique trunk and fender script. New carpets were installed, the door panels were rebacked, new padding was fitted to the dash. In all, the project took some two years. The result: a unique one-off prototype that survives as a prized possession of its lucky owner.

Dutch Darrin's proposal for a Packard sports tourer didn't get very far. It would have been nice, though.

Last Days in the Bunker:

Packard's Plans for '57

Packard's Detroit factory on East Grand Boulevard had been built in optimistic spurts commencing in 1903, when the company moved from Ohio to become a serious automobile manufacturer. In its heyday, this was one of the most beautiful, well-ordered industrial plants in the country. Its interior, painted a uniform Packard Gray, was spotless, and was peopled by a workforce of high morale. Its facade, visible on the tree-lined boulevard, was studded with enormous pillared entryways, each bearing the marque name in dignified block letters, almost like a mausoleum. And a mausoleum it almost was in the summer of 1956. Packard production had ground to a halt after customers had drifted away over the years to Cadillac, Lincoln, and Imperial. There was hardly anything left except the styling studio, still valiantly working on the "big" 1957 Packard. Designer Dick Teague, a car enthusiast devoted to the marque, portrays this period as "the last days in the bunker."

That summer, financial sources had dried up one after another. Gradually, the big plant was emptied by layoffs and personnel shifts to Studebaker's factory in South Bend, Indiana. Said Teague in an interview published in *Packard: A History of the Motorcar and the Company:* "Styling was the last to go because, I think, those who were manipulating us thought there

was some chance. You knew goddam well the end was close, but you kept hoping for the life raft. Rumors? You wouldn't believe the rumors that circulated. Everybody from Universal CIT to Ford was buying us out."

Under wraps in the bunker was the 1957 Packard—not a pretender to the name in a Studebaker uniform, but the real thing—the car with which James Nance had hoped to rebuild the luxury end of the business. There were numerous renderings and clay models, and an actual running prototype—all based on the distinctive Predictor dream car, which had appeared on the show circuit in 1956.

Built for Packard by Ghia of Turin, the Predictor had been designed under the aegis of chief stylist Bill Schmidt, and strongly reflected Teague's thinking. It was advanced for its time—about three years ahead, really—with a wrapover-and-wraparound windshield, quad headlights hidden behind clamshell doors, and fenders level with the hood and rear deck. The lines were chiseled, with an almost extruded look. Many ideas from Teague's former Packard show cars were evident on the Predictor, notably a retractable, reverse-slant backlight; tall "cathedral" taillights; and a smart ribbed molding that ran from the front around to the bodysides. The traditional Packard grille shape was preserved in a narrow, vertical central "nose." Sliding panels were built into the roof over the doors to ease entry and exit; these could also be left open for ventilation with the doors closed and windows rolled up.

Inside, the Predictor was all convenience, with electronic pushbutton Ultramatic transmission; electric servos for opening the decklid, roof panels, and windows; and individual contoured seats with reversible cushions, leather on one side and fabric on the other. The roof sail panel had portholes, just like contemporary Thunderbirds, decorated with courtesy lights and a jeweled escutcheon. The emblem, a "V" on a circle, was created by Teague, who was searching for a timeless symbol like Mercedes-Benz's three-pointed star.

The Predictor was powered by a 300-horsepower Packard V-8, and was ostensibly driveable. But Ghia had botched the electrical system, and getting any of that fancy equipment whirring was a gamble that often ended in a short circuit or great clouds of smoke. These problems could have been worked out in production. In fact, the Predictor was the inspiration for Studebaker-Packard's 1957 line.

Advance planning envisioned a three-tier body-sharing program: a 130-inch wheelbase for Packard and Packard Executive; 125 inches for Clipper; and 120 inches for Studebaker. The Executive was, in effect, to be a detrimmed Patrician, and was considered part of the senior series. In March 1956, the Clipper was omitted, and would have continued with the '56 body dies for one more year. Later, the plan was changed again so it would share Studebaker President dies.

The body-sharing idea was quite brilliant (if not exactly original), because all three makes would be able to use a common inner shell and many exterior sheetmetal pieces. The Clipper's hood, roof, doors, and front fenders would interchange with the Studebaker's, for example. There was even a thought of a Ranchero/El Camino-type pickup, using these panels and a few unique panels for the cargo bed. It was a gameplan on the grand scale of General Motors—S-P's last attempt to cast itself as a "full-line" producer.

The Predictor's influence was quite apparent in all the '57 models, Packards particularly. The Clipper had a more "styled" appearance, as Bill Schmidt wanted it to appeal to younger buyers in the Mercury-Oldsmobile market. Studebaker would continue to compete in the low-price field with Chevrolet, Ford, and Plymouth.

Under the program envisioned for '57, Packard would have had the same model lineup as in '56: a four-door sedan in Patrician and Executive trim; Caribbean, Four Hundred, and Executive two-door hardtops; and a Caribbean convertible. A four-door Patrician/Executive hardtop would have been added for 1958, and the Executive would have been divided into standard and deluxe series. The Clipper, after going through '57 as a holdover 1956 model, would appear for '58 with all-new sheetmetal and two- and four-door hardtops in standard and deluxe form. These

Built by Ghia, Teague's Predictor show car inspired the '57s.

Ford picked up the Predictor's reverse-slant rear window for the '58 Continental.

"Black Bess," the development mule, was torched by the company in 1956 after all hope failed.

would not have been called Packards: the Clipper name had already been registered as a separate make. Studebaker would have offered all of the above body styles in 1957-59, plus a station wagon and a Hawk sports model in both pillarless and pillared coupe styles. The Hawk had been derived from Raymond Loewy's Starliner/Starlight coupes which first appeared in 1953. An Express Coupe would have come along in

The '57 Packard would have had an enormous rear deck, huge fins, and an Edsel-style vertical grille. This is a rendering for the Four Hundred hardtop.

Last Days in the Bunker

'58 as an addition to Studebaker's line of light- and medium-duty trucks.

From an engineering standpoint, the '57 Packard would have been an advanced version of the 1955-56 model, with self-adjusting torsion-bar suspension. The Packard V-8, with a displacement 374 cubic inches in 1956, would have been bored out to 440 cid for '57, good for at least 300 bhp.

There was even a plan to revive a twelve-cylinder Packard, last seen in 1939. According to Richard Stout, former member of Packard Product Planning, the V-12 would have been built using V-8 tooling to save money. As Stout wrote in *The Packard Cormorant* magazine: "Eight of the cylinders would be bored, then the block moved to do the remaining four. The block was a 90-degree type, 30 degrees off for in-step-firing V-12s. To compensate, each throw was to be split and staggered 30 degrees to provide in-step firing. This split throw would be similar to the principle

President Nance's interest in classic-era prestige caused Styling to look at 1930s body styles, like this Town Cabriolet.

This is how the '57 Caribbean might have looked. All "senior" Packards would have worn rear fender skirts.

Buick used to make its existing 90-degree V-6 into an in-step-firing engine." Displacement, using tooling from the 320-cid Clipper engine, would have been 480 cid, just seven cubic inches over that of the 1939 twelve, but with much "squarer" bore-and-stroke dimensions.

Another remarkable but unworkable dream for the big 1957 Packard was the "radar brake." This consisted of a small radar sensor mounted in the grille and connected to an electric screwjack that engaged or disengaged the brake pedal independently of the driver. Wrote Stout: "Demonstration consisted of driv-

ing the car directly at a wall . . . The radar brake performed effectively. [But later], a company official drove the experimental Four Hundred home. On his first right turn the sensor picked up a cross-traffic car waiting for a light. Screech! Halt! Recovering, our shaken driver proceeded down a narrow street with parked cars, two-way traffic and pedestrians—all of which alarmed the sensor . . . Our official was astounded . . . The trip home was forgotten as he made a beeline for the company garage."

The V-12 wasn't as impractical as the radar brake,

If S-P's fortunes had been different, this Patrician Four Hundred four-door hardtop would have followed for '58.

Predictor influence is clear in this rendering of the Four Hundred two-door hardtop. That's Teague's "classic" emblem on the roof pillar.

Last Days in the Bunker

but when Nance failed to obtain finances for his grandiose three-year body-sharing program, it disappeared along with the rest of Packard's plans. The engine tooling would have cost only $750,000, according to Stout.

In those trying days in the summer of '57, the only tangible evidence of all this scheming was a running prototype of the new big Packard, nicknamed "Black Bess" by its builders. Said Teague: "It was a mule [that] looked like it had been made with a cold soldering iron and a ball peen hammer. And it was . . . a last-ditch effort to come up with some money for die models. The doors opened, but it was a very spartan mule. [Engineer] Herb Misch had put it together. There wasn't anything old on it except the V-8, and that was modified . . . It's flowers on the grave now, but it might just have saved Packard." Before 1956 was out, the company despairingly put this prototype to the torch.

Teague's story about the fate of poor Black Bess is one of those poignant, bittersweet tales that abound in Detroit. Misch called Teague one day and told him to see to the car's destruction: "It's all over," Misch said—but he didn't have the heart to carry out the "execution." Teague called Red Lux, "an old welder in the studio, who had been there since the cornerstone. There were two or three other cars in the studio, including another black one, a Clipper. I said, 'Okay, it's official, cut the black one up.' I came back around 4 p.m. and he was just finishing. The pieces were lying all around like a bomb had gone off. It was probably the dirtiest trick I ever played but I said 'My God, Red, what have you done? Not *this* one, man, the one over in the corner!' The poor guy had to have had a strong heart, because if he didn't he would have died right there. His face drained, and when I told him I was just kidding he chased me around the room. You've got to have a sense of humor in this business." That must have been what kept Teague and his colleagues sane during those last days in the bunker.

Clipper probably would have kept its 1955-56 body in '57, then switched to this design for '58. It was no great loss.

The Cars That Couldn't Have Saved Studebaker

Some of the proposals in this chapter have been optimistically called the "designs that could have saved Studebaker." In truth, these cars-that-never-were wouldn't have saved anybody. The first of these appeared in 1963, and by then it was too late to save Studebaker's car business by any means. In December of that year, the South Bend, Indiana factory closed its doors. Production was then shifted to the "rump" plant in Hamilton, Ontario, where Studebakers were built in low volume until early 1966. After that, the marque was gone for good—a victim of sporadic mismanagement over the previous 40 years. Studebaker was badly served. Every time it recovered from one disaster, management seemed to come along with some decision sure to produce a fresh setback.

Most of the designs shown here would have been welcomed by other manufacturers. Put into mass production under more astute management, these stillborn Studes would probably have been successful. They were certainly unique, imaginative, and intriguing; and some of them were exactly right for the times. Indeed, they're pretty much right for the times even today.

Industrial designer Brooks Stevens of Milwaukee had known Studebaker president Sherwood Egbert since his days at McCulloch. Stevens had been called

in after Egbert took over the helm in 1961, assigned to clean up the 1962 line and remake Studebaker's image. It was a crash program, less than year long. Stevens produced the exciting GT Hawk using the old Raymond Loewy hardtop tooling, which dated back to 1953. He also reskinned the Lark, and continued to improve its looks for that model's last two seasons. But these were nothing compared to the all-new Studebakers conceived by Stevens for 1964, '65, and '66.

"As soon as Sherwood Egbert called me in to facelift the '62s, our studios got to work on projections for all-new (or at least new-looking) Studebakers for 1964-66," Stevens said. "By degrees, each more radical than its predecessor, these cars would have replaced the Lark—falling at the Cruiser end, the big end of the intermediates. The wheelbase would have been 116 inches, later adding 113 inches. We planned to continue the 289 V-8; though it was old, it was a good engine, and with a blower it went like hell. We put it into the chassis, mounted farther back for better weight distribution, and prepared three prototypes . . . a wagon, sedan, and hardtop coupe. Each model had two different sides representing standard and deluxe versions."

Egbert eyed what Stevens had done with approval, and asked the designer if he could commission a brace

Studebaker

of full-size steel prototypes. The company was in dire financial straits, and all it could allocate for the job was $50,000. Stevens decided his only hope was Italy—and not a coachbuilder like Pininfarina, either. In Turin, he found himself at a small coachworks known as Sibona-Bassano. "I walked in," he remembered, "there was laundry on the line and chickens running around. I took these two little guys out and fixed them up with Camparis. We got good prices out of them—$16,500 per car, an incredibly low figure." Surprisingly enough, the three finished prototypes would have done justice to a much more famous coachbuilder. Stevens called them "jewel-like," and said Egbert was very excited about them.

The 1964 proposal, least radical of the trio, was a station wagon that displayed a sliding rear roof panel like the one Stevens devised for the '63 Lark Wagonaire. Its grille was similar to the 1962-63 Lark's, only wider and squatter, and its hood and deck were extremely low. Taking into account Studebaker's limited budget, Stevens opted to save both the company and its customers some money: the wagon's doors were diagonally interchangeable (right front to left rear,

left front to right rear) and the bumpers were identical front and back.

The interior of the '64 proposal was a modest development based on the 1963 Lark, which had introduced a sharp new oblong gauge cluster with full instrumentation and rocker switches for the minor controls. The prototype also had an oblong cluster, but it was made up of three planes instead of being flat; the outer ends were angled in slightly toward the driver, as on the GT Hawk. The area around the gauges was illuminated so the cluster acted as a courtesy light when the doors were opened. The doors themselves were very thin, giving the car tremendous interior room for its compact exterior dimensions.

The 1965 prototype was a more advanced version of the proposed '64 model, this time a sedan. Its square, recessed grille was complemented by Cibié rectangular headlights, though rectangular units were then illegal in the U.S. Again, the doors were diagonally interchangeable but on this car they were also cut into the roof for better entry/exit. A clever touch was the use of one-piece hood/front fenders and trunklid/rear fenders, which provided exceptionally good access to the engine and luggage compartments.

The inside of the '65 concept car was an evolution of the '64 interior, with an upright instrument nacelle,

1964 proposal was this wagon with lines derived from the '63 Lark.

"Wagonaire" roof was used on the wagon prototype which wore "Skyview" script.

Stevens' proposal for '65 was this four-door sedan which carried Lark Cruiser identification. Door panels were diagonally interchangeable.

complete with a full set of straightforward white-on-black gauges, mounted squarely in front of the driver. The rest of the dash was a padded shelf that contained a sliding vanity/glovebox. The radio and clock, which would have been options on a production version, appeared as two clear bubbles mounted on top of the dash. This was so that if they were not ordered, there would be no unsightly blanks in the dash. Radio on/off and volume were controlled by pressing down on the bubble; stations were selected by turning it. The clock bubble rotated, so that either driver or passenger could see it clearly. The steering wheel had a tilt feature, which was still uncommon in the early '60s.

Clearly, the most innovative and stylish of the three was the proposed 1966 design, which Stevens hoped would usher in a new generation of Studebakers. This was done as a hardtop, and was seen as a replacement for the GT Hawk. Stevens dubbed it Sceptre. Though its shape was a conventional notchback, the Sceptre was extremely low, with acres of glass and several singular features. Instead of conventional headlamps, it had a single full-width tube designed by Sylvania, which Stevens found gave better highway illumination than sealed-beams, without the glare. Another tube at the rear carried full-width taillights. Besides giving the car a lot of glass, Stevens had come

up with the trick of making the rear roof pillar partly out of blue polarized glass. From the outside, the pillar appeared to be opaque metal, but occupants inside could see out through it.

The Sceptre was equally striking on the inside. All instruments except the speedometer were encased in bubbles, and each could be tilted for maximum driver visibility. The speedo was a strip-type affair perched atop a short stalk that jutted up from the minor dials for easy reading. The center console was angled toward the driver for optimum reach. Like the '65 proposal, the Sceptre's dashboard was very clean, with a lot of padding that again concealed a sliding vanity. The passenger's side formed a "rally" table. The seats were vinyl buckets, the center sections done in chrome-like mylar. Had it entered production, the Sceptre would likely have been the most modern American car on the road in 1966.

Unfortunately, it never had a chance. Sometime in 1963, Stevens related, the money started to dwindle: "Around that time a bell rang and we were suddenly told we'd just have to reskin the existing Lark again . . . Of course, you never dared stop. So we kept going on the prototypes even then." But the project was shelved at the end of 1963 with the closure of the South Bend plant.

'65 sedan featured one-piece hood/fenders and rear deck/fenders.

With its 116-inch wheelbase, the '65 Stude would have been very roomy.

The Sceptre two-door hardtop was to be the new-generation '66 Studebaker. Prototype had different trim each side. This is the "deluxe" version.

Unusual dash, angled console, and slim buckets made the Sceptre sleek inside.

Studebaker

Also in the running for Studebaker's 1965-66 line were a pair of prototypes based on the beautiful Avanti coupe. They were built under the direction of Raymond Loewy, who, like Stevens, had been retained by Egbert. While Stevens was busying himself with a facelifted Lark and Hawk, Loewy had conjured up the fiberglass-bodied Avanti. Like Stevens, he also proposed a new line of Studebakers, and went overseas to get prototypes constructed. While Stevens chose an obscure Italian coachbuilder, Loewy picked the obscure French house of Pichon-Parat, near Paris. A notchback and a fastback were completed, each done with a two-door configuration on one side and four doors on the other.

During 1963, Loewy worked hard trying to persuade Egbert and other Studebaker executives to put these cars in the hopper for the '65 or '66 model year. There was no money, of course, though the proposals were practical—and different. Clean and handsome, they bore the Avanti's imprint, and would have been a logical follow-up to that sensational sporty car. Both

prototypes still exist in South Bend; one was recently refurbished for display at the Studebaker Century Center. Both were well-finished originally with full interior upholstery, though dashboard "gauges" were merely decals.

The only problem with these proposals—aside from the company's lack of money—was the car that inspired them. The Avanti was becoming a miserable commercial failure—and some ex-Studebaker people say that wasn't entirely because of production delays. Former body engineer Otto Klausmeyer noted: "The fastback prototype should have been built [first], instead of the Avanti ... Yet the Avanti was in production, and had been abundantly rejected by the public, before the sedan prototypes were finished ... The directors would not approve the sedans because they feared the Avanti influence would be the kiss of death, not because they were a bunch of provincial sod-busters, as most articles about these cars imply."

Last, but not least, were Studebaker proposals for 1967-69, again the work of the persistent Brooks Stevens. Determined to save the South Bend plant and its work force, Stevens met hurriedly in early 1964 with former Ford executive Charles Sorensen to plan a revolutionary new small car with a very spacious interior and a 113-inch wheelbase.

This car, variously called "Familia" and just "Studebaker," took Stevens' ideas about interchangeability to the extreme: the hood/trunk, doors, bumpers, headlight/taillight housings, windshield/backlight, and side window glass were all interchangeable. Sorensen's contribution was a small, simple production line suitable for producing the unit-body fiberglass car—a real eye-opener. He invented a carrier that held four half-body molds, and moved them to individual stations for the fiberglass gel coat, outside matting, reinforcement matting, and bake oven curing. The device turned and positioned the bodies, and ended by bringing them back to starting point for removal. With this machine, the interchangeable panels, a simple proprietary en-

Full-width taillight strip was matched by headlight bar up front.　Rear roof pillars were fitted with one-way glass.

The "Familia" made the most of interchangeable body panels. In Stevens sketch it wears the Lark label.

Loewy did two Avanti-style prototypes. This one was a fastback.

Prototype on the left was mocked-up as a four-door on one side.

gine, and minimum frills, the car would have a unit cost, Stevens and Sorensen calculated, of just $585. It could probably have been profitable with a retail price of about $1100.

"I had tremendous hope for this idea," Stevens said. "I took the project to the board at the end of February 1964, and they were quite interested. Unfortunately, the financial backers had just breathed a sigh of relief after dumping automobiles at last. There was no way any money was going to be made available for anything on wheels. I quit in disgust. I guess it was too late. It was certainly the wrong time to try."

Both Loewy prototypes were left upstairs at South Bend. This photo was taken in 1971. The Avanti II was a success by then.

Tucker:
Too Good or Too Bad?

It was cold in Chicago that windswept Sunday in January 1950, and for some, it was the same inside the U.S. Courthouse on Adams Street. After one of the most bizarre fraud trials in history, the jury was out—had been for some time. The defendants fidgeted, awaiting the eventual decision—all that is, save Preston Thomas Tucker. Yet the impending verdict could bring him a cumulative jail sentence of 155 years, and fines totaling $160,000.

Fortunately for Tucker, the jury cleared him of all charges—31 counts of conspiracy, mail fraud, and illegal stock procedures. He vowed to build another car, and some designs for it were commissioned. But they never went beyond a drawing board. In 1956, Preston Tucker died of cancer.

The "Tucker 48," was at the heart of the controversy. Hailed as "The First Completely New Car in Fifty Years," it was announced in 1946, although an actual prototype didn't appear until the following year. To war-weary America, expecting bold new ventures in almost every sphere, it did seem a notable achievement—tomorrow's car today.

The Tucker represented a dramatic break with automotive tradition. Styled by free-thinking Alex Tremulis, who had literally been given a free hand by Preston Tucker, it didn't look like anything else on the road. Its combination bumper/grille, first of its kind, rode low under the fenders and a sharply pointed hood. Instead of the usual two headlights, there were three:

the center one, called a "Cyclops Eye," turned with the wheels to cast a beam in the direction the car was steered. The hood concealed not an engine—that was in the rear—but a sizable luggage compartment.

In plan view, the Tucker was a fastback. Unlike other torpedo styles of the day, its fenders did not follow body contour, but jutted out firmly toward the rear. They were capped by three-sided taillights and punctuated at their leading edges by air scoops for the engine. Out back was another functional grille above a more conventional bumper and three pairs of exhaust pipes.

The inside was as different as the outside. Tucker believed in safety above all, and personally specified the interior design, which was finalized by Tremulis. All gauges were grouped in a large circular dial directly ahead of the steering wheel. Flanking them left and right were controls for lights, heat, ventilation, and the like, all recessed and well out of the passengers' way in a crash. Door panels contained conventional window winders along with an ashtray and glovebox, but door handles were eliminated in favor of safety pushbuttons. The area ahead of the front passenger was a large, carpeted, partly padded box, which Tucker called a "storm cellar." The idea was for the passenger to be thrown into it (willingly or unwillingly) in a crash to avoid injury. In the unlucky event someone hit the windshield, it was designed to pop out of its frame rather than shatter in place. The interior was comfortable as well

Here's the air-cooled Tucker engine. It gave 166 bhp.

safe—well-upholstered and spacious—with doors cut into the roof for easy entry and exit in what was a very low car for the late '40s.

The Tucker broke with tradition in its mechanical layout, too. Power was provided by a 166-bhp flat six (horizontally opposed cylinders) made of aluminum alloy, and rear-mounted for near even weight distribution. The frame rode below the centerline of the wheels, and carried independent suspension front and rear. The pounds-to-horsepower ratio was lower than on any American car yet developed.

The Tucker carried its name in large letters on the rear bumper, which is where the drivers of most other cars saw it first. There's no doubt the car was a tremendous performer. As an example, the late Bill Hamlin of California, a longtime Tucker devotee, took his then six-year-old car to the Los Angeles County Fairgrounds for a test in 1954. The track record for the standing quarter mile was held by an Oldsmobile 88—78.8 mph—that was on hand to defend itself in a drag race. At the flag the Olds took the lead, but Bill had decided to start in second gear rather than risk his Tucker's transmission. In seconds, the Tucker was ahead, setting a new record of 82 mph for the quarter mile.

The few Tucker road tests conducted suggest typical 0-60 mph acceleration of 10 seconds flat, with 100 mph reached in 33 seconds. The 10th car built (out of 51, including the prototype) made three two-way runs at Bonneville in 1950, averaging 131.64 mph—with a 4.31:1 final drive. With more conventional, numerically lower gearing (on the order of, say, 3.50:1), the Tucker seemed capable of 150 mph: if it wasn't, it was still in the Jaguar class in 1948. Yet this was a full-size,

six-passenger four-door sedan. From these figures, it's easy to see why the Tucker caused so much excitement in the early postwar years. And to top it all, Preston Tucker told the press that he would sell the car for around $2500.

For awhile it looked like Tucker was going to succeed. He rented the largest plant under one roof, sold $15 million worth of stock, and built 50 "production" cars (really little more than prototypes), all of which performed impressively. But then the enterprise dissolved into a quagmire of resignations and charges of "fast-sell" tactics, followed by a government investigation, and the previously mentioned trial of Tucker and seven of his colleagues.

The question of whether Preston Tucker was serious, crooked, or just misguided remains debatable even today. But there's little debate about the car: it was an advanced machine with praiseworthy features. If not exactly beautiful, it certainly looked purposeful, and it had that phenomenal performance. But what about the collapse of Tucker's business? How much did the big Detroit producers have to do with it—and how much is traceable to Preston Tucker himself? Despite the murkiness surrounding such questions, some fairly safe conclusions are possible.

Consider a comparison between Tucker and the other company that launched a postwar onslaught on Detroit, Kaiser-Frazer. Like Tucker, K-F began with a little known promoter, Joseph W. Frazer, but one with

Tucker

industry experience at Chrysler and Graham-Paige. Frazer lacked cash, so he teamed up with Henry Kaiser, the wartime shipbuilder backed by the best banks and credit available. Tucker didn't find an angel of equal stature, though it's interesting to wonder what might have happened had Tucker teamed up with Kaiser.

K-F's initial capitalization was $52 million—and that wasn't enough. At the time, Chevrolet was setting *twice* that much aside just for its new 1949 models. Kaiser later admitted he should have started with around $200 million. Tucker raised $15 million. K-F needed 18 months from incorporation to get its first cars off the line. It took Tucker 2½ years. K-F needed six months after moving into its new plant to get its earliest pilot models completed; it took Tucker 18.

K-F's first full year of operation, 1946, saw no cars until June, but ended with 12,000 built, and was followed by 140,000 units in 1947. Tucker's first full year, 1947, saw no cars, and only 50 were built in '48. K-F's maximum work force reached nearly 20,000. Tucker predicted he'd hire 35,000, but never employed more than 2000.

K-F floated two stock issues by satisfying the Securities and Exchange Commission. Its prospectus admitted that its program was a gamble, but stated what the company had done already and what it hoped to accomplish. Tucker's firm floated one stock issue, and promptly created a mess for itself by making several false statements and unsubstantiated claims. Tucker was caught fiddling with the books, making indirect payments to promoters, and planning to assign work to his mother's Ypsilanti, Michigan machine shop, which didn't have the capacity. And the SEC never let him live down these actions.

Preston Tucker liked Tremulis' proposal for a revival called the Talisman, but died before it could be built.

Rear grille was a distinctive, functional feature.

Engine was behind the rear axle line, and was fairly accessible.

Like Tucker, Henry Kaiser put his son on the board, and no one blinked an eye. And like Tucker, Henry eventually got into trouble with a stock issue—his third. But that was only after one of the underwriters, Cyrus Eaton, decided it wasn't backed up by the ability to deliver—like Tucker's stock.

Like Tucker, Henry Kaiser promised a car with unit construction, torsion-bar suspension, and an unorthodox drivetrain. But unlike Tucker, Kaiser went to more conventional engineering and abandoned the far-out design in order to get production going. Kaiser mapped out an assembly line covering millions of square feet and two stories of factory with the help of an ex-Chrysler production engineer, and began building 200 cars a day right from the start. Tucker sent 50 cars down a conveyor, and called *that* a production line.

Tucker put in a bid for the idle Republic Steel blast furnace in Cleveland with the War Assets Administration, and was told his figure was high. But in August 1948, the WAA awarded the plant to Kaiser-Frazer. Tucker cried foul, but the agency said it wasn't convinced he could pay for the facility while Kaiser could—and did.

It has been said that Tucker didn't know the "right people" in Washington as Henry Kaiser did. But the truth is that K-F's Washington lobby in those days was very often Joe Frazer, who didn't know all the right people, either. Frazer once sat all day in the office of WAA administrator Jess Larson just to get an interview—a resourceful and patient piece of good business. Preston Tucker never displayed that kind of patience or tact.

If the comparisons with Kaiser-Frazer aren't enough, take a look at the timing of important events in the Tucker's history. The Chicago plant was acquired in 1946, yet the stock application didn't come until June 1947. Tucker sold the stock in September of that year, but was still trying to decide on an engine the following

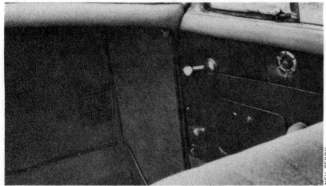
The carpeted "storm cellar" and padded dash rail were safety features.

The center "Cyclops Eye" headlight turned with the front wheels.

The Tucker would leave other cars behind. Maybe that's why nameplate was at the rear.

Front "hood" lifted to reveal a fairly roomy luggage bin.

Unified instrument and control grouping was innovative.

Rear Fender vent (left) doubled as a fuel filler flap.

Tucker

spring (original plans called for a 589-cid air-cooled unit). The first Tuckers were completed in March 1948, but by August when the plant closed, only 50 had been built despite Tucker's claims of a working production line and his promise to build 1000 cars a day by mid-1948.

It would appear, then, that Preston Tucker may have been brilliant, but he made promises he couldn't or wouldn't keep. This alienated some of his best associates. When patent attorney and board chairman Col. Harry Toulmin quit the company in September 1947, he objected to Tucker's "fast-sell" practices, such as promoting stock on the basis of an unfinished prototype. Vice-president Herbert Morley testified at the trial that $800,000 in receipts were unaccounted for in 1947, and that he had argued with Tucker in 1948 over his mother's inability to build transmissions, let alone engines, at her Ypsilanti Machine and Tool Company. Even Alex Tremulis, who warmly respected his engineering ability, recalls that, for a time, Tucker kept insisting on impractical ideas—independent front fenders that turned with the wheels or a rearview periscope device, for example.

The old song about General Motors doing in the little guy has often been heard in connection with Tucker. His own well-publicized charges and paid ads in defense of his company referred to some dark, clandestine attempt to thwart him. In those haphazard days after the war, anybody with an idea and a little money for advertising could pose as a major entrepreneur, selling stock in a corporation set up to produce . . . nothing. The SEC had its hands full with promoters like Tucker. And it didn't like announcements from someone they already thought suspicious that they were part of a plot to "get" him.

For the record, Sen. Homer Ferguson of Michigan, and his Michigan appointee to the SEC, Harry MacDonald, leaked word of the forthcoming Tucker investigation, and prejudiced the Chicago automaker. After all, they were from Detroit, and like most politicians could be expected to protect the interests of their local constituency. Even so, the company already had a history of SEC violations dating back to its first stock issue.

If Tucker was as sincere as he claimed, why was he nearly without friends by the time of his trial? Somewhere along the way, he must have alienated a lot of people. Those who left the corporation invariably left in a huff, later denouncing him for promising more than he could deliver. Those who remained were found on opposite sides of the courtroom at the celebrated trial.

Preston Tucker, said *Special-Interest Autos* magazine in 1973, "was essentially a small-time promoter who'd gone big-time. He was out of his pond. He remained a stranger and perhaps even a threat to the SEC, and he didn't know anyone in government. He was careless in some of his pencilwork, perhaps in a bit of his talk, too, and when the SEC jumped on him about those initial 15 irregularities, the irregularities did exist."

That opinion seems completely reasonable. Nevertheless, Preston Tucker did devise one fantastic automobile. Nevertheless, the government did overreact, despite all he had done to invite it. Nevertheless, even if GM didn't try to stop him, certain representatives of the state of Michigan did.

The Tucker thus remains something of an enigma in automotive history—a car that appeared to be, but in reality never was. Perhaps it should have had a better chance to succeed. Happily, there are many Tuckers in the hands of collectors today. At this writing in fact, 49 of the 51 made—including the "Tin Goose" prototype—are known to exist, and Tucker enthusiasts are still looking for the other two. That is an overwhelming survival rate. Perhaps Preston Tucker really had something there after all.

Tucker's chief designer Alex Tremulis is shown in his studio in this 1948 photo.

A Case of the Willys

The little unit-body Aero-Willys, conceived by former Packard engineer Clyde Paton and styled by Phil Wright, was one of the outstanding postwar compacts. It was faster than the Henry J, roomier than the Nash Rambler, as solid as the Hudson Jet, and better-looking than any of them. The Aero sold reasonably well during its first year, 1952. But after ailing Kaiser Motors Corporation bought Willys-Overland in 1953, the Aero-Willys went to the wall along with the Kaiser. The writing on that wall was plain: a demoralized dealer force; a doubtful public, fearful about buying a possible orphan; and an undeserved reputation for service problems. The last U.S. models, the Bermuda hardtop and Custom sedan, were made in 1955.

Like every other auto company that failed to survive, Willys had lots of plans for future models. Photographs and records of these did survive, at least, and show that American buyers missed out on some of Willys' best products when the production line ground to a halt.

Willys would have added a station wagon for model year 1955 had it remained independent, for '56 as initially projected by Kaiser management. And it was to be a wagon with a difference—a true hardtop-wagon, not a pseudo-hardtop like the Chevy Nomad. The design was 100 percent conventional Aero from the beltline down, but dispensed with the normal fixed B-post. The area from the windshield to the "C" pillar,

which curved down and rearward aft of the rear seat, was open. Had it come off, Willys would have beat GM with a hardtop-wagon, scoring a major industry first.

Scheduled farther down the line was an ultra-sleek hardtop derived from the basic Aero by company stylists. Only one illustration of this car has been found, but it whets the appetites of those who appreciate good form. Obviously much lower and sleeker than the Aero, it sported projectile-like front fenders, with deeply frenched headlights, a low hoodline, and lots of glass. Sadly, it was just another idea that was not to be.

Two people who figured significantly in Willys' final days as a carmaker were Howard A. "Dutch" Darrin and Duncan McRae. McRae was the young stylist who had translated Darrin's radical ideas for the 1951 Kaiser into reality back in 1948, and he was still with Kaiser when that firm acquired Willys in 1953. Just before he left for Ford, McRae created a facelift for the Aero. This was marked by a noticeably downsloped hoodline, which may have inspired the smooth hardtop previously mentioned. A beltline molding swept from headlamp rim back to the rear fender, where it joined an inset taillamp.

Darrin, working separately on a freelance basis, proposed another facelift that was kind of a cross between the Henry J and his Kaiser sports car—possibly on purpose. When Kaiser bought Willys, it found itself with two compact models. Darrin's proposal may have been an attempt to relate the two lines

A Case of the Willys

stylistically by starting with the better-looking Aero body and frame. The changes included longer rear fenders carrying rakish vertical taillights above a prominent rear bumper. Up front was a small "rose-bud" grille, not very different from that of the Kaiser-Darrin. The front wheel wells recalled the Henry J theme, and were similarly sculptured.

Given the usual three-year lead time for getting new designs production-ready, both Darrin and McRae were probably looking at these facelifts for 1956, or '55 at the earliest. Neither proposal would have been particularly costly or difficult to tool up. As things developed, of course, there was no reason for pushing ahead with anything. By early 1955, the decision was made to discontinue both Kaiser and Willys passenger cars in the United States, and to concentrate strictly on Jeep utility vehicles. The Kaiser (see Chapter 19) duly went to Argentina, where it was built from 1958 through '62.

The Aero-Willys had a second life, too—in Brazil. Built by a local company, Willys-Overland do Brasil, it featured 1955 front- and rear-end styling, with 1954 side trim. As proof of its basic design merit, this handsome little car stayed in production for a full decade after the first models went on sale.

Darrin's proposed Aero-Eagle facelift featured enlongated rear fenders remarkably like the 1953 Studebaker coupes.

Darrin's front-end revision would have looked like this.

The neat hardtop-wagon would have been a Willys first.